PSYCHIATRY
FOR BEGINNERS

▶ **EIA ASEN**

▶ **ILLUSTRATED BY BERNARD CANAVAN**

Writers and Readers

WRITERS & READERS in association with **UNWIN PAPERBACKS** London · Sydney

UNWIN ® PAPERBACKS
40 Museum Street, London WC1A 1LU, UK

Unwin Paperbacks
Park Lane, Hemel Hempstead, Herts HP2 4TE, UK

Writers and Readers Publishing
Cooperative Society Limited
144 Camden High Street, London NW1 0NE, UK

Writers and Readers Publishing Inc.
500 Fifth Avenue, New York NY 10110

Allen & Unwin Australia Pty Ltd
8 Napier Street, North Sydney, NSW 2060, Australia

Unwin Paperbacks with the Port Nicholson Press
PO Box 11–838 Wellington, New Zealand

ISBN 0 04 616030 2

Printed in Great Britain by
Richard Clay (The Chaucer Press) Ltd,
Bungay, Suffolk

Contents

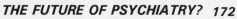

THE STORY SO FAR. . .

Many people associate psychiatry simply with mental hospitals, drugs and couch. Some think it's only for the idle rich who can afford it, and others see it solely as an instrument of social control dealing with the misfits of society.

Officially, psychiatry is that branch of medicine which deals with those people whose problems or symptoms are regarded as being 'mental' – no matter whether they are physical, psychological or social in origin. To do this psychiatry has been awarded public status through legislation (Mental Health Acts). It has been given certain powers and institutional bases: primarily the mental hospital and also, more recently, local psychiatric units in general hospitals.

Psychiatry as a specialised discipline and social institution, concerned with the identification and treatment of 'mentally abnormal' individuals, is of fairly recent advent: it did not exist, as such, before the 18th century. It was between 1750 and 1850 that society's response to the deranged changed dramatically: madness became mental illness. And mental illness, since it was defined as an illness, became the province of the medical profession. And people defined as being mentally ill were hurled into specifically created institutions, the lunatic asylums. How and why did it happen? And why then?

Before the end of the 18th century mad people had not been treated as a distinctly separate group of deviants. Instead, mentally disordered people might have ended up in institutions together with criminals, fools, eccentrics, women with red hair, physically ill, poor vagabonds and political extremists. They had been grouped together with other misfits but many, if not the majority, of the insane were still at large in the community.

Some 100 years later the insane had been clearly distinguished from other 'problem groups'. They were physically isolated from their communities, incarcerated in a specialised state-supported asylum system. Here their problems became diagnosed predominantly as medical and, logically, they had been taken care of by a new group of professionals: the 'mad-doctors'.

Before then medical interest in and management of the mad was rare. Of course, the idea that madness was a disease had been entertained sporadically by many different cultures at different times. But no previous cultures and societies had ever developed any coherent approach, in theory or practice, supported by legislation, towards those of their members regarded as mad. Yet madness was by no means a phenomenon with which other times and cultures were not acquainted. It was called by all sorts of different names, such as madness, insanity, lunacy, etc., but the difference was that these madmen were not systematically isolated, categorised and then assigned to specific treatment programmes.

In other words, though some of the phenomena which we now call madness have been observed for a long time, psychiatry is just 200 years old. Before then the medical approach to lunacy was much less developed, and had to compete with theological, demonological, philosophical or educational perspectives.

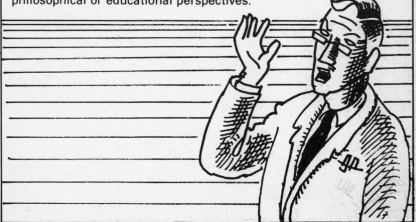

To understand how and why psychiatry came into being as an increasingly organised body of theory and practice, a social institution with its existence formalised by law, we need to concentrate on the following questions:

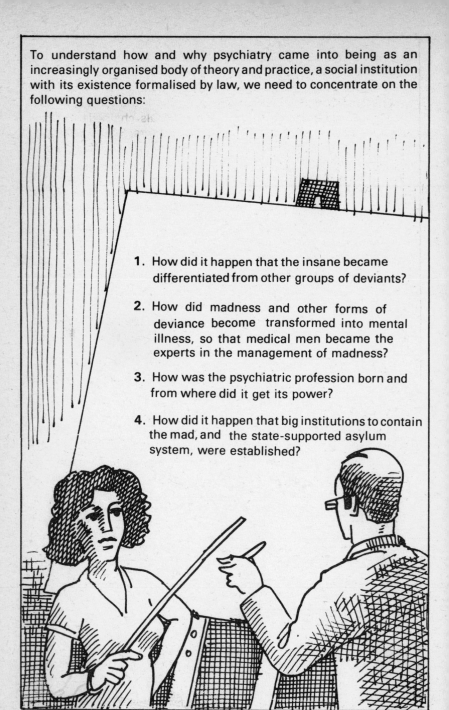

1. How did it happen that the insane became differentiated from other groups of deviants?

2. How did madness and other forms of deviance become transformed into mental illness, so that medical men became the experts in the management of madness?

3. How was the psychiatric profession born and from where did it get its power?

4. How did it happen that big institutions to contain the mad, and the state-supported asylum system, were established?

To answer these questions one needs to write the history of psychiatry. This could be done in many different ways.

For instance, 'As madness is a universal phenomenon, each society has had to find ways of dealing with it. In the dark middle ages mad people were treated no better than animals, chained to the wall. But once upon a time, some enlightened doctors decided to free the madmen from their chains. These doctors started to reform the cruel system of madhouses where the mad were inhumanely treated. New treatment methods were found which were scientifically tested and this eventually led to the mental health system as we know it now. Psychiatry and its patients lived happily ever after....'

Another way of looking at the history of psychiatry is to place it in its historical and political context. After all, the birth of psychiatry coincided with the new Industrial Revolution.

The *Industrial Revolution* with its new technology and changes in family life, its new demands on people, went hand in hand with major social changes: a break-up of the predominantly rural society, the crowding of people into towns. The new industries needed an ever-increasing number of able workers. New criteria of 'reason' were created: the worker had to function like one of the new machines — without arguing, engaged in repetitive and monotonous work, reliable, disciplined, uniform and self-denying.

This of course in itself produced a new generation of disturbed, useless and eventually psychologically disordered people. Moreover, there was no room for people who did not fulfil the requirements of the big machinery: only 'productive' people could work in factories. Unproductive people had to be accommodated elsewhere.

The development of an industrialised society meant the growth of a single national market and the emergence of central political authority. Local communities now had to define themselves as parts of a larger political and economic system. This meant that no longer was it possible simply to get rid of deviants by passing them on elsewhere. Instead new local ways of containing or segregating deviants had to be found. The accommodation of the unproductive became a more organised and specialised business.

Most early madhouses were privately run for profit. Private madhouses flourished as the upper classes were prepared to pay to avoid the embarrassment of having daily contact with their mad relatives. Speculators from many different backgrounds looked for easy profits, and also imposed their own views of 'reason'.

The mental hospitals, or lunatic asylums, were run by a great variety of people: doctors, teachers, priests, chemists, lawyers, philosophers, soldiers, merchants and others. Long cures for madness were elaborated, with the aim of curing the whole individual: mind *and* body had to be tackled at the same time. The standard treatment methods in lunatic asylums of the 18th/19th centuries had been in use for many hundreds of years, and some of them are still in use in psychiatry today though under different names. They included:

Consolidation:
prescribing tonics (an emphasis on strength and vigour).

Purification:
herbal extracts 'to clear the blood', getting rid of heavy blood by bloodletting, the use of soaps, vinegar and laxatives.

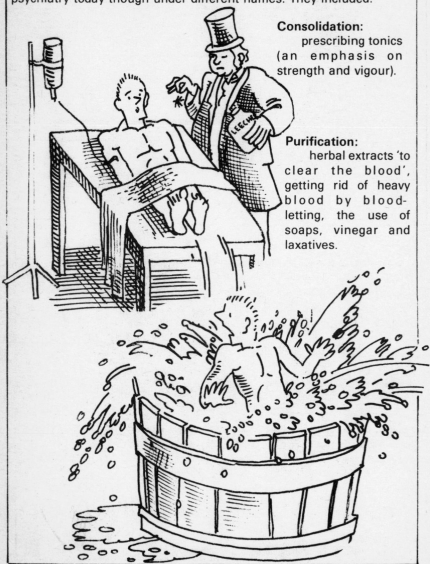

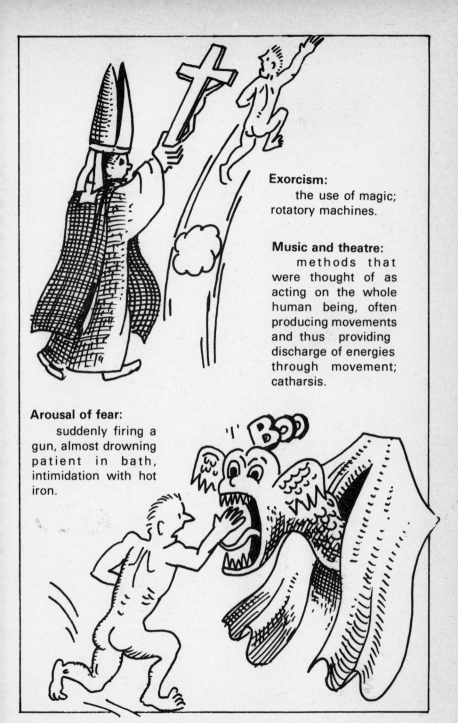

Exorcism:
the use of magic; rotatory machines.

Music and theatre:
methods that were thought of as acting on the whole human being, often producing movements and thus providing discharge of energies through movement; catharsis.

Arousal of fear:
suddenly firing a gun, almost drowning patient in bath, intimidation with hot iron.

Surgeons, physicians and apothecaries were increasingly attracted to the lucrative 'trade in lunacy'. They often claimed that they had unique medical methods to achieve cures for many types of bodily dysfunction, and it was only a small step to claim that such remedies would also cure the insane. Doctors had the advantage of being seen as possessing powerful remedies whose use demanded special training and expertise — and the idea of expert intervention restoring the deranged to reason was attractive in a climate of growing respect for scientific expertise. But in order to take advantage of this position, medical men had to support some of their claims.

Certainly the fact that then (as now) one third of mental conditions 'spontaneously remit' (i.e. improve for no apparent reason) could be used to 'prove' the success of treatment methods. The publication of books on insanity helped, and so did the fact that 'insanity treatment' was included in medical curricula, so that some students could in fact claim some 'proper' training.

Gradually the vague cultural construct of madness was transformed into a formally coherent, scientifically distinguishable entity, which was seen as caused by a single underlying pathology. The alliance with medicine and the natural sciences lifted the status of psychiatry and lent it some authority.
Mind matters were reduced to brain matters.

But the early psychiatrists didn't initially have too smooth a ride. There was some competition, partly from non-medics. A number of reformers had become increasingly concerned about the often inhumane 'treatments' to which the mad were exposed.

In England, in 1751, William Battie founded St. Luke's Hospital as part of the movement against Bedlam — that notorious reservoir of madness which implemented many of the above 'medical' treatments. Battie summarised his new approach: 'Management did much more than medicine'. His emphasis was more on care than 'cure'.

Battie influenced William Tuke (1732-1819) who in 1796 founded the Retreat in York. There the 30 patients were treated as guests; 'kindness and tolerance formed the accepted practice', in an atmosphere free from any direct medical influence, with fresh air and rural surroundings. The aim of treatment, 'moral' as it was called, was to teach the madman the 'salutary habit of self-restraint'. This was done largely by appealing to the patient's self-esteem: the patient had to join tea-parties with the superintendent in his best clothes and converse in the appropriate fashion. He was not allowed to behave in 'a childish or...... domineering manner' but had to be a 'rational being'. The external physical and chemical straight jackets had been replaced by internal 'moral' ones.

The purpose of 'no restraint' was to encourage the individual to reassert his powers of *self*-control, and so enable the lunatic to approximate the bourgeois ideal of the rational individual. A system of rewards and punishment taught the insane to obey the dictates of a 'civilised' morality.

The Retreat was a success: it proved that the asylums could be a comfortable environment. Warm baths and kindness in place of 'scientific' remedies, with good results, administered by laymen. Moral treatment could have posed a threat to 'medical' psychiatry. It never became a coherent theory but rather remained a pragmatic approach which could be incorporated as a humane addition into the body of psychiatry.

Because of its emphasis on non-technicality, it did not encourage the emergence of an organised professional group. Thus medicine was able to reassert itself and establish its dominance.

By the middle of the 19th century psychiatrists began to organise as a distinct profession. Since laymen questioned whether medical control of asylums was appropriate, psychiatrists had to lobby support, which wasn't altogether easy given their failure to establish the efficacy of medical forms of treating the insane. Nonetheless, with the Acts of 1828 and 1845 the medical profession acquired virtually total control over the right to treat the mentally disordered. By 1851 the Association of Medical Officers of Asylums and Hospitals had been founded and two years later it was publishing its own Asylum Journal. These were important events as they gave the new profession some kind of credibility in the eyes of the public.

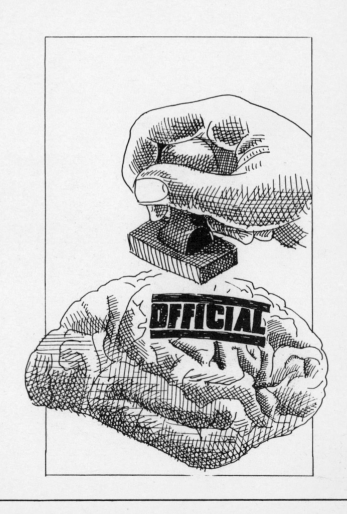

The 1845 Lunatic Asylums Act stipulated that every county and borough had a statutory obligation to provide 'adequate' asylum accommodation for its poor insane within a few years. And indeed, within a short space of time dozens of asylums were established.

Despite the fact that the medical profession had adopted some of the ideas of moral treatment alongside its own medical cures, the initial strong influx of mental patients meant a dilution of many of these principles. Self-discipline soon became the enforcement of obedience — and regularity was translated into the celebration of order. The important features of moral treatment soon disappeared and the asylums became glorified prisons — custodial institutions of wide dimensions.

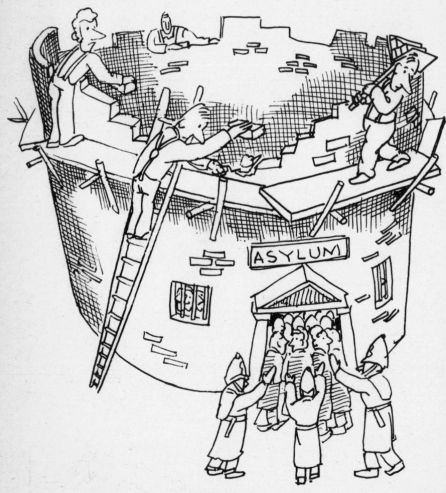

Hand in hand with the building of asylums went the rising number of recorded madmen. One reason for this certainly had to do with the new awareness of the problem of madness: a new system of observation and enquiry had led to the detection of cases previously unreported. A second reason may well have been the new stresses of industrialism. A third reason: advances in medicine had led to the prolongation of lives which would otherwise have been short. Fourthly, the asylum by its very existence became a dump for all sorts of inconvenient people: families as well as the community at large could abandon the struggle to cope with the troublesome. Their tolerance changed as there was suddenly an easy way out — and the new notion of what was intolerable of course widened the definition of what constituted mental illness.

Increased demand expanded the asylum system and the expansion of the asylum system created increased demand for its services. Doctors did not of course object: more cases meant more justification for their existence. This reinforced their role of becoming the experts for the management and classification of the insane, and the more cases they saw, the more objects of study were available. The more objects of study, the more material from which to develop elaborate theories.

The rapid increase of people admitted to lunatic asylums provoked *The Times* in 1877 to warn, 'If lunacy continues to increase as at present, the insane will be in the majority, and, freeing themselves, will be able to put the sane in asylums'.

21

By the second half of the 19th century asylums were sprouting all over Europe. The concentration of large numbers of allegedly insane people made it possible to study their common characteristics as never before.

Scientists were now looking for physical causes of mental symptoms, and there was a tremendous breakthrough when the cause of syphilis was discovered. Suddenly it was possible to explain some mental disorders as resulting from a syphilitic infection of the brain. This was a promising start as a large proportion of mental hospital inmates were suffering from syphilis. Establishing physical causes for mental disorders also meant relieving the patient from guilt feelings about being a moral or social failure.

Now scientists were searching more than ever for a physical basis to all their patients' mental symptoms. Positivism came to dominate medicine: it postulated that the laws governing human life are similar to those governing the rest of nature. This implies that not only are the human sciences capable of constructing theories on the same causal, deterministic basis as the natural sciences, but also that our mental life and social relations can be studied objectively, like any object in the natural world.

To achieve this the madman could no longer be seen as a person who behaved abnormally in certain situations at certain times. Instead he was reduced to a 'case', with symptoms more 'interesting' than he himself could ever hope to be.

As pathology became a special discipline in medicine, doctors became more interested in the history of a particular disease process than in the personal history of a human being. Interest shifted from the sick to sickness. Psychiatrists did well to link themselves with the natural sciences. By the late 19th century, positivism was the most powerful force in much policy-making, and it was in the interest of those dealing with the insane to adopt it in order to get maximum support.

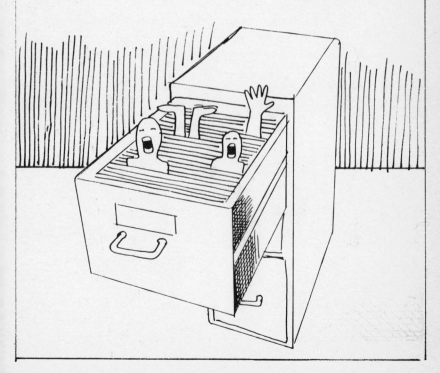

Another intellectual development of great significance for psychiatry was Darwin's theory of evolution. This was used by some writers to support the 'degeneration' hypothesis, by which a variety of social problems could be attributed to the hereditary transmission of constitutional aberrations and weaknesses, with the severity of the disorder increasing with each generation.

Thus Morel concluded that intoxication (alcohol or food poisoning) and social corruption could contribute to a 'nervous disposition'. The children of a nervously disposed parent would inevitably develop a neurosis, in the following generation a psychotic breakdown would happen, and all this would finally result in idiocy in the children of psychotics.

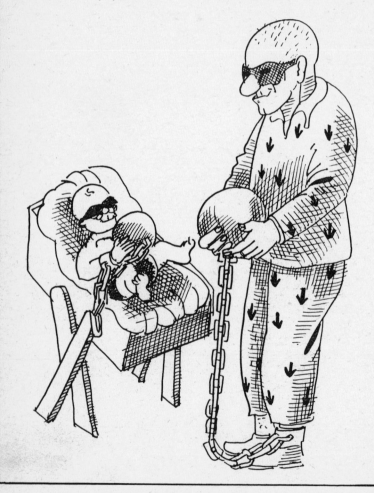

The development of psychiatry was not dissimilar in other parts of Europe.

In France, Philippe Pinel (1745-1826), by 1793 director of the Bicêtre asylum, exclaimed: 'I am convinced that these madmen are so intractable only because they have been deprived of air and liberty.' He took off their chains and replaced them with his 'traitement moral' which was similar to that of his English colleagues. There may have also been another motive for Pinel's reforms — he saw himself as a scientist and wanted to study madness, simply by observation, unhindered by physical restrictions.

Pierre Charcot (1825-1895) a major figure in the latter half of the 19th century, specialised in treating patients suffering from a complaint which he labelled 'hysteria': some of these patients had paralysis of limbs, anaesthesias of parts of the body, epileptic seizures or other types of convulsive fits. Through the technique of hypnosis he enabled some of his patients to regain control over their bodies. He could not isolate any organic causes, suspected that 'C'est toujours la chose genitale' ('It is always something genital') but he didn't know how or why, and then suggested that hysteria was based on a hereditary disease of a certain brain structure.

Like so many psychiatrists before and after him, he was not really interested in his patients' fate. They served as vehicles for his ideas. He gave spectacular Tuesday afternoon lectures at the Salpêtrière which were attended by the élite of Parisian society. Here he made young women perform in public epileptiform convulsions and hysterical movements. Disorders induced in susceptible personalities with constant repetition of these performances led to more serious mental disturbance — a model for some aspects of case conferences and demonstrations today!

In Germany, **Emil Kraepelin** (1856-1926) laid the foundations of modern descriptive psychiatry. He applied the methods of medical enquiry and classification to many mental symptoms as displayed by large numbers of chronic hospital patients, the incapacitated and institutionalised. He was interested in the statistical analysis of large numbers of similar 'cases' in order to arrive at a systematic classification of psychiatric disorders.

He identified two major psychiatric illnesses: dementia praecox (later to be re-named by Bleuler as 'schizophrenia') and manic-depressive illness. Kraepelin argued that these mental illnesses ran a typical course from onset to conclusion and he postulated that this was the result of some kind of organic dysfunction — a degenerative process, endocrine dysfunction or toxic invasion.

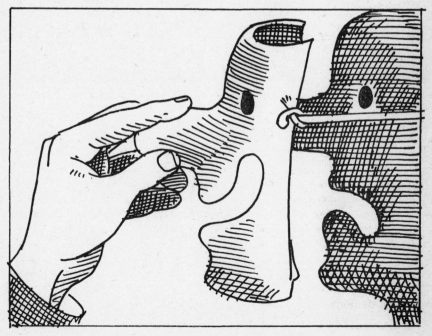

At the end of the 19th century, psychiatry was dominated by the neuropsychiatric model: mental disorder was thought of as being due to physical causes producing disorder in brain nerve cells which then resulted in mental symptoms. 'Insanity is in fact disorder of brain producing disorder of mind' said Henry Maudsley, a leading figure in early British psychiatry. Psychiatrists saw themselves as neurologists (nerve and brain specialists) believing that psychiatry had inevitably to progress to neurology, from mind to brain.

Both Kraepelin and Charcot subscribed to the neuropsychiatric model of mental disorder. Their pupils started off with the very same model but soon went in different directions:

Kraepelin's students formulated the organic approach;

Charcot's pupils, and in particular Freud, laid the foundations for the psychodynamic approach.

AN EXAMINATION OF PRESENT-DAY PSYCHIATRY

In contemporary psychiatry we find a number of different theoretical and practical approaches. They are based on certain belief systems with regard to the genesis and meaning of symptoms, and this of course influences the treatment plans.

Many of the concepts and therapies will not strike the reader as particularly 'modern' (especially if the reader has carefully read the previous chapter!) But what is modern is that some of the concepts and treatment methods have been systematised.

The organic approach

The organic approach developed out of the neuropsychiatric model. It has the longest tradition and is the most influential one in hospital psychiatry. Its main hypothesis: there are no psychological changes in the individual without changes in the organic structure and function of the brain. Physical causes have psychological effects.

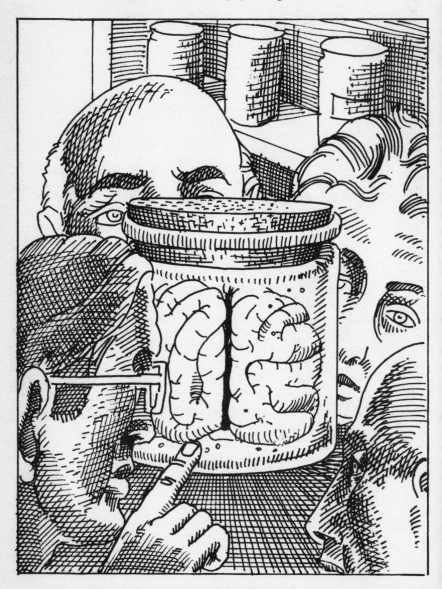

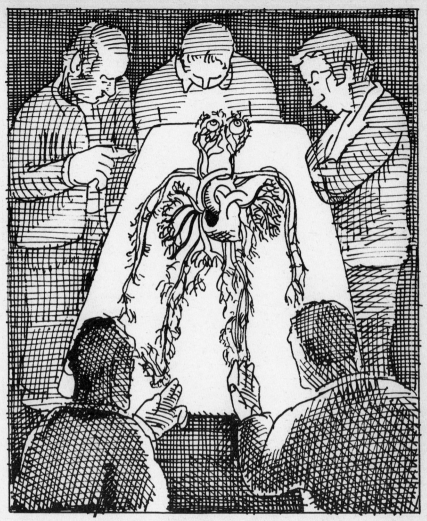

'Organic' does not just mean the brain; it refers to the biochemical, physiological, neurological, anatomical, endocrinological, genetic and other factors involved in the causation of mental disorder.

Since Kraepelin's day psychiatrists have managed to relate a number of psychological disturbances to organic disorders such as epilepsy, arteriosclerosis, acute toxic states (drugs and alcohol), genetic and nutritional disorders, infections, brain injuries and tumours.

A number of such conditions are now regarded by psychiatrists of all persuasions as organic disorders producing psychological symptoms.

Some organic psychiatrists believe that it is only a question of time and research until all mental problems can be explained as physical abnormalities. Take schizophrenia....

In the past three decades many different research teams all over the world have managed to 'identify' — often under dramatic circumstances — 'it' (the alleged physical cause): the virus, enzyme, hormone, toxic substance, gene, organic deficiency responsible for schizophrenia, only to find out later that none of their hypotheses survived the critical test.

So much about the theory. The treatment methods of the organic approach reflect the theory: they are 'physical' — drugs, ECT and psychosurgery.

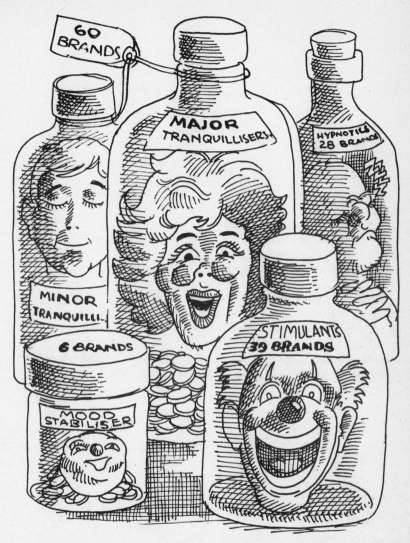

The drugs used in modern psychiatry aim at altering mood and perception, the level of consciousness and intellectual functioning. The choice of drug depends on the diagnosis made; antidepressants for depression, minor tranquillisers for anxiety, major tranquillisers for severe psychological disturbance, hypnotics for sleeplessness, stimulants for lethargy and mood stabilisers for fluctuating moods.

Advocates say:
Our research is highly scientific and funded by reputable drug companies. These drugs work! We have theories about how they work upon specific processes in the brain.

Critics say:

The research is biased or simplistic.

The 'initial improvement' often observed is a 'placebo' effect: the patient's expectations and wishful thinking make him respond not so much to the actual drug prescribed but to the doctor as drug, or to having a *new* treatment.

Drugs create unrealistic hopes in that they claim to get to the bottom of the problems when all they can usually do is suppress them, for some time.

Drugs are often claimed to treat isolated problems or illnesses which lie outside the patient's responsibility ('Hit the depression — not the patient' says one notorious drug ad.). The patient becomes infantilised, passive and dependent: all he needs to do is to swallow a drug which will fix him up again.

Both psychiatrist and patient invest their hopes in miraculous drug 'cures' — a belief in part created and perpetuated by pharmaceutical companies and advertising.

Most drugs have side-effects: these are unintended and often insidious in their ill-effects. At their worst they can cause additional serious illness.

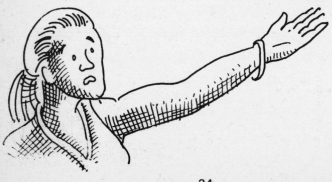

But both organic psychiatrists and their critics believe that, under certain circumstances, the use of drugs is in fact necessary. Except by using brutal physical force, there is often no other way of containing an over-excited psychotic patient: major tranquillisers (phenothiazines) sedate the patient. Many psychiatrists also claim that if it weren't for long-term phenothiazine treatment, some long-term patients could not live outside mental hospitals. Lithium seems to be helpful to patients with dramatic mood swings and prevents frequent hospital admissions.

Also it would be wrong to think that it is solely the psychiatrist who wants to force tablets down his patients' throats. Many patients demand an 'organic approach', something 'concrete' for their disturbance, and may make a psychiatrist who doesn't believe in drugs feel cruel and narrow-minded.

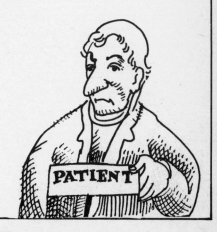

Electro-convulsive treatment (ECT) is the modern variation of an old theme: the belief that people could be shocked out of their misery (see historical part, p.13). The patient receives under general anaesthesia an electric shock lasting about 3 seconds: a current is applied to the skull leading to convulsions. This general 'shake-up' is meant to be therapeutic.

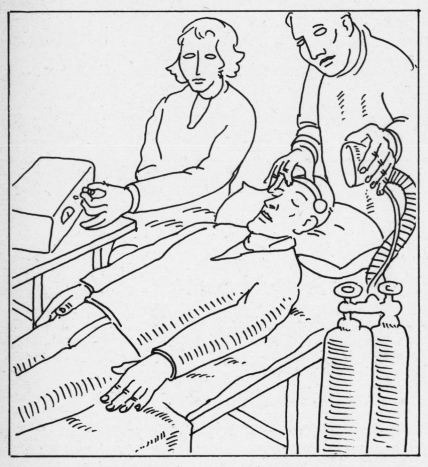

Psychiatrists who believe in the use of ECT find it particularly effective when treating patients with severe depressions. They see it often as a life-saving treatment method, and a course of ECT usually consists of 8 separate shock sessions, spaced out over a period of 4 to 6 weeks. The first effects the patient subjectively notices on waking are giddiness, confusion and impaired memory.

The critics of ECT attack the brutality of the act and the lack of understanding of how it works and how much damage it can cause. They see it as a form of corporal punishment. They also point out that ECT is occasionally used as a diagnostic tool: the response to ECT ('I feel so much better, doctor, you don't have to give me any more treatments') confirms for some psychiatrists the diagnosis of ' endogenous depression ', and this then justifies the use of ECT retrospectively — a way of circular thinking which is not unusual among psychiatrists. But it must also be mentioned that some patients get addicted to ECT (or just the anaesthetic?): they often push their psychiatrists to give them the beloved treatment. Some patients have achieved up to 200 treatments.

The third major method of organic treatment is psychosurgery. Discoveries made during the wars of this century showed that the personality can actually change as a result of physical injuries: a bullet shot through the frontal part of the brain, for instance, could turn an inhibited obsessional person into a 'couldn't care less' character.

Some brain surgeons made use of this insight and developed the techniques of lobotomy and leucotomy. At first large cuts were made into the brain tissue which connects the frontal lobe with other important brain centres.

More recently the techniques have been refined to include small (microscopic) lesions, and the use of radioactive metal brain implants. Psychosurgeons claim 'good results' 'in cases of severe, intractable depression, anxiety states and obsessional disorders'.

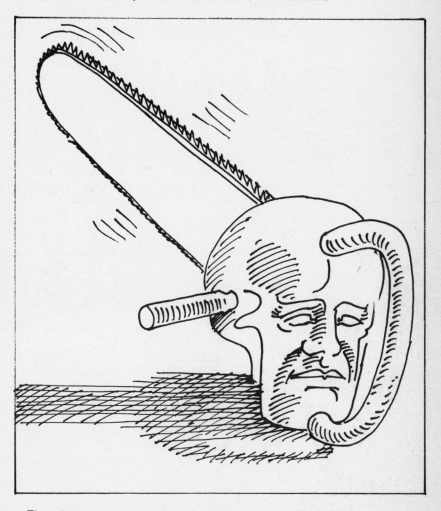

The above mentioned forms of treatment are 'performed' on the passive recipient, the mostly patient patient, while the following treatment forms require a more active stance on the patient's part.

The psychodynamic approach

This refers to a range of approaches stemming from psychoanalysis.

Psychoanalysis was the creation of Sigmund Freud (see the EXCELLENT *Freud for Beginners*). A contemporary of Kraepelin, he was committed to the scientific ideology of his time: initially he believed that mental disorder could be explained in biochemical and neurophysiological terms.

He tried to understand and treat certain complaints for which there were at the time no satisfactory explanatory models. A pupil of Charcot, Freud was interested in hysteria.

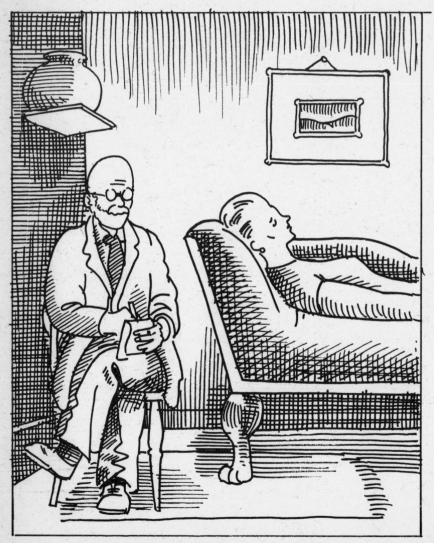

Freud's ideas developed beyond the scientific framework of his day. He thought that there was more to the mind than met the eye: not just a conscious but also an unconscious part — the world of dreams and fantasy. His theory went like this:

There are certain thoughts, wishes and anxieties which are not conscious. If they became conscious, they would cause conflict or disturbance.

But the forces behind secret wishes are very strong: they are the drives, and particularly 'libido' – the energy attached to the sexual drive.

An example: the little boy's wish to have mummy all for himself has to be repressed i.e. put into the unconscious part of his mind.

If the boy had given in to his wishes, perhaps....

Instead....

But these thoughts would continue to nag underneath it all and could come to the foreground again in later life.

When studying adults Freud often discovered such childhood wishes. He thus claimed that early unconscious wishes and the resulting unresolved conflicts persisted far beyond childhood and were reflected again and again in the person's adult life, sometimes finding expression in the form of symptoms.

In the treatment situation the psychoanalyst tries to understand the unconscious conflicts that underlie the patient's problems or symptoms.

The patient (let us assume it is 'he') tries to talk about whatever comes to his mind. Sometimes his mind will seem empty, or his chain of thoughts will not seem to lead anywhere. He may find other ways of not talking about what matters, and of hiding himself from the analyst.

These barriers, or types of resistance, can often be traced back to relationships which the patient had with some important figure in his early life; 'old' feelings are being transferred on to the psychoanalyst, a phenomenon known as transference.

Psychoanalytic treatment very much relies on the development, analysis and interpretation of the transference: the analyst points out to the patient how he transfers old conflicts or secret wishes from years back into the 'here and now' of the sessions and on to the psychoanalyst.

An example: P starts the session by talking about colour schemes for his new house. After listening for a while, the analyst tells P that he is avoiding talking about the things that really matter here in the session. The patient replies weakly, 'But all this matters to me!'

The analyst sees this as evidence of resistance, but is not going to say so at this point. The patient then proceeds to talk about his boss at work, this bossy man, who always puts him down, wanting to know better, humiliating him to the extent that he finds it occasionally very hard to restrain himself and not explode and hit his superior.

The psychoanalyst, after careful consideration and after gathering further evidence to support his hypothesis, then interprets the 'material' (as the patient's talk is called) in the following way:

'You are telling me how cross you are with your boss, and perhaps indirectly you indicate to me how cross you are with me, thinking that I always want to know better, or even put you down. And this is how you interpreted my comments earlier on. This type of thing, despite your protestations, may make you in fact quite cross, but you daren't confront me as you may be worried as to what might happen. You fear that you may even explode and hit me. And all this may link up with similar feelings you talked about earlier, concerning your father, being afraid of speaking your mind for fear of causing a violent argument.'

The treatment situation with the psychoanalyst is thought to be representative of all such important situations and relationships, evoking early responses and feelings.

To get to the point where a patient is less dominated by his fantasies about life is a long process — often many years with regular attendances of up to 5 times per week, 50 minutes each. Each session can be very hard work for both patient and analyst, and few people are both able to afford the money and willing to make the commitment.

Psychoanalysts believe that for patients to get in touch with their inner world they need to lie down and not see the analyst, who usually sits behind.

The analyst acts to some extent as a kind of blank projection screen upon which the patient projects his own inner world. This requires analysts to show as little of their own personal selves as possible. That way the patient's attitude towards the analyst can be seen most clearly as the patient's constructions.

Some offshoots of psychoanalysis

Carl Jung (1875-1961) was once Freud's disciple and collaborator. In 1912/13 he broke away from Freud (because of disagreements about the libido theory) and developed his own 'analytic psychology'. Jung rejected Freud's sexual hypothesis as reductionist and instead broadened the libido concept to include creativity and the search for the self leading to individuation.

His emphasis was less on the physical world and more on the spiritual and religious aspects of life: universal symbols or 'archetypes' were seen as the manifestations of the 'Collective Unconscious', cutting across all times and cultures.

Jung's approach, though initially developed in a mental hospital, has not had a great impact on theory and practice in 'public' psychiatry.

Wilhelm Reich (1887-1957) took Freud's concept of libido in a particular direction: the ability to have a complete orgasm was seen by him as being essential to a healthy body and mind. His treatment approach subsequently focused less on the mind and more on the body, especially on how to get through the 'character armour' of tense musculature, the physical means by which people kept their own sexual needs in check.

(Reich is also well-known for his attempt to use Freudian theory in the service of Marxist politics. See *Reich For Beginners*.)

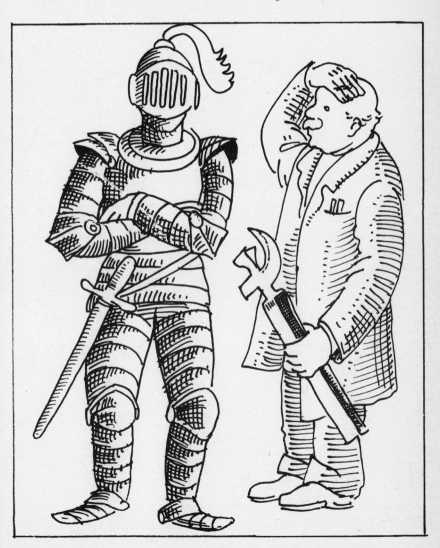

Psychoanalysis itself has continued to develop since Freud. Some psychoanalysts see Freud's theoretical framework as being still basically an adequate one, whilst others have argued the need for major revisions.

More attention is now given (especially by the *Kleinian* school) to very early experience and to the importance of mothering (Freud had been more interested in the father). Exploration of the *unconscious* remains the corner-stone of psychoanalysis.

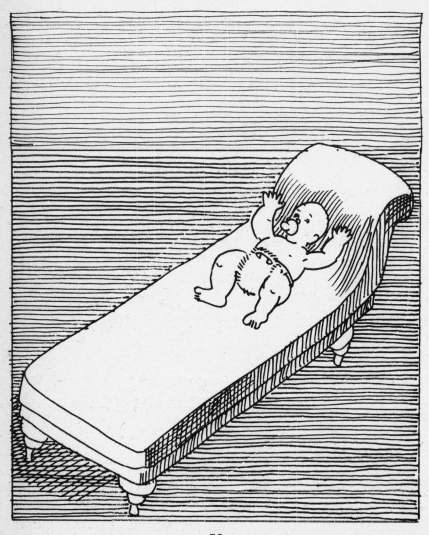

PSYCHOTHERAPY

This term now covers a very wide range of practices. It may be based firmly on psychoanalytic principles, differing from psychoanalysis only in being less intensive (usually once or twice a week) and less ambitious e.g. it may be aimed at achieving relatively specific changes within certain areas of the patient's life. The couch is rarely used.

It may alternatively be directed not at the unconscious but at the conscious parts of the mind only. Rather than 'working in the transference', the therapist may seek to relate to the patient more as a friend or adviser. Some patients may be seen as having little capacity to *change,* in which case the aim of the therapy would be supportive. Here the distinction between psychotherapy and 'counselling' sometimes becomes blurred; the latter term may refer either to more supportive or to more actively therapeutic work.

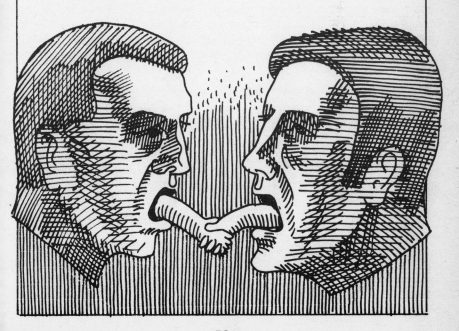

The behavioural approach

The behavioural approach explains normal and abnormal behaviour in terms of learned responses to environmental stimuli.

Ivan Pavlov (1849-1936) tried to explain learning by formulating the principle of classical conditioning. Pavlov found that he could provoke a dog to salivate by ringing a bell. The sound of a bell does not normally cause a dog to salivate. However, if on a number of occasions the bell is rung and simultaneously food is placed in the dog's mouth, the bell will eventually elicit salivation on its own, in the absence of food.

Or, to put this more theoretically: a certain stimulus (food) provokes a certain response (salivating). If a new stimulus, the conditioned stimulus (bell), is paired with the first, unconditioned stimulus (food), then the response will be 'associated' with both stimuli and can therefore be elicited by the conditioned stimulus alone.

In the US the psychologist **John B. Watson** (1878-1958) sought to base a comprehensive theory of *human* behaviour on Pavlov's principle. To demonstrate that neurosis was the result of conditioning, he set about producing a neurotic symptom in a child. He chose little Albert, 11 months of age. A phobia of white rats was induced in the infant by standing behind him and banging an iron bar with a hammer every time he reached for the animal. The child reacted with fear, and after a number of such pairings of rat with noise, the child reacted towards the rat by withdrawing and crying. He simultaneously became afraid of a rabbit, a dog and cotton wool.

The concept of classical conditioning could explain certain forms of learning, but it did not explain others — for instance 'trial and error' learning. B.F. Skinner (1904 -) introduced in 1938 the theory of *operant conditioning*.

A rat is placed in a special box, on one wall of which there is a lever which, when pressed, will reward the rat with food. After exploring the box for some time, the rat will accidentally press the lever and so obtain food. This may happen a few times before there is any noticeable change in the rat's behaviour, but gradually it will begin to press the lever more frequently. It will not be deterred if the rewards (or 'reinforcements') are intermittent.

Both classical and operant conditioning explain maladaptive behaviour, whether this is social deviance or mental disorder, as the product of faulty learning.

If one can learn maladaptive responses, then it must also be possible to un-learn them! And it must also be possible to learn adaptive behaviour! Behaviour therapy or modification is based on these principles. Behaviour therapists focus entirely on the symptom: the symptom *is* the illness or disorder.

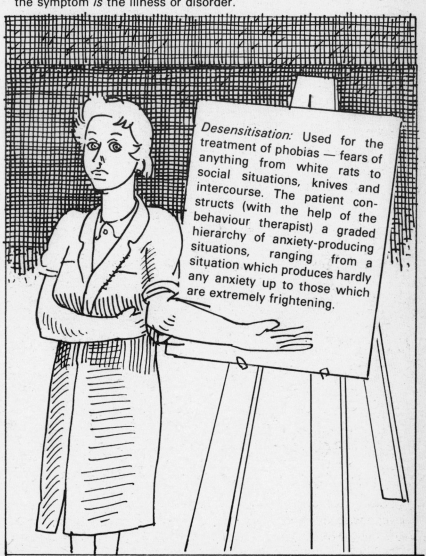

Desensitisation: Used for the treatment of phobias — fears of anything from white rats to social situations, knives and intercourse. The patient constructs (with the help of the behaviour therapist) a graded hierarchy of anxiety-producing situations, ranging from a situation which produces hardly any anxiety up to those which are extremely frightening.

Muscular relaxation is first induced (usually through relaxation exercises) and the patient is then asked to visualise an anxiety-producing situation starting at the bottom of the hierarchy (minimal anxiety). Providing the patient remains relaxed, the next situation up on the anxiety ladder can then be imagined.

This goes on until the strongest anxiety-provoking stimulus can be imagined without anxiety. Desensitisation in imagination may be combined with graded re-training 'in vivo' i.e. with exposure to real life situations.

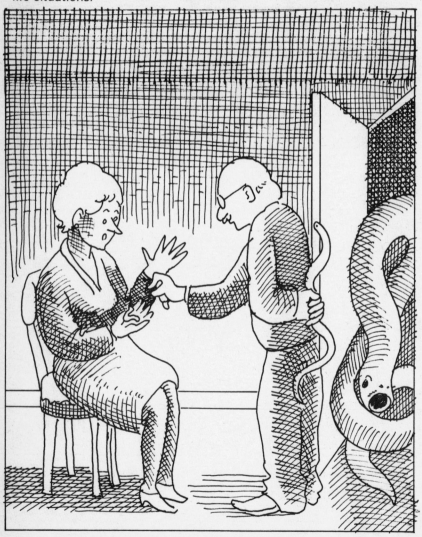

Flooding: Also used as treatment of phobias. The patient is intensively exposed to major anxiety-producing situations. This can be done in imagination or in vivo. The hope is that the anxiety will burn itself out.

Modelling: This involves imitating a model behaving in a relaxed fashion in the presence of a feared situation or object.

Social skills training: Trying to teach people how to behave in certain social situations, how to be assertive, how to know what to say and do after having said 'hello'. (In some ways not unlike the 'moral treatment' of old!)

Token economy: An application of Skinner's 'operant conditioning'. Behaviours necessary for efficient day-to-day functioning (e.g. unaided washing and dressing) and 'appropriate social responses' are encouraged by giving rewards for their performance. Used on some long-stay mental hospital wards. A form of token currency is established and the patient is 'paid' in tokens for desired behaviour. The tokens can then be exchanged for small luxuries or privileges.

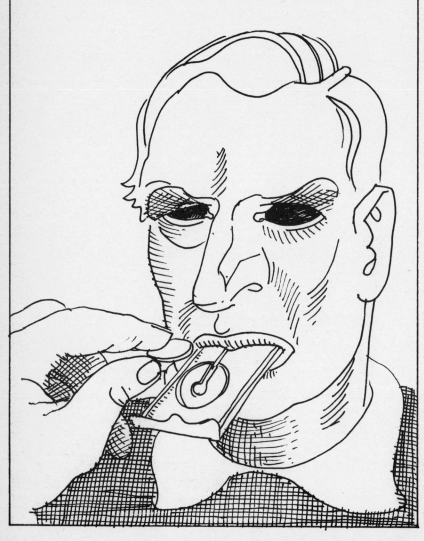

Aversion therapy: A noxious stimulus, usually an electric shock or a drug which induces nausea or vomiting, is paired with the circumstances which evoke the undesirable behaviour, or is applied when the behaviour itself occurs. Used for treatment of deviant sexual behaviour, alcoholism, gambling, smoking, and also certain behaviours in the mentally handicapped.

Behaviour therapists, or behavioural psychotherapists, as some nowadays like to call themselves, believe in the effectiveness of these methods. They usually have impressive statistics to support their beliefs. As they set out to treat the 'symptom' their assessment of the effectiveness of behaviour therapy is measured in terms of the presence or disappearance of this target symptom after the course of treatment.

The critics find this a very naïve approach. Psychodynamically orientated psychiatrists particularly will expect 'symptom substitution' (the replacement of one symptom by another) as the underlying problems (giving rise to the symptoms) have not been dealt with.

The critics also claim (rightly or wrongly) that people actually differ from rats and they therefore reject treatment methods which they see as a re-programming of the human rat. Furthermore, these critics see the behavioural approach as a dangerous technology, open to abuse by psychiatrists and embodying a superficial, manipulative approach to human suffering.

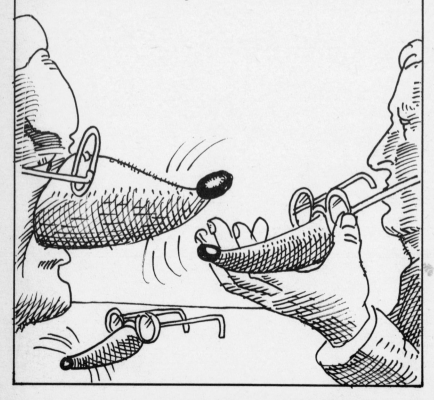

Cognitive therapy: The growing disillusionment with conditioning as a model for human behaviour, combined with an emphasis on the patient's beliefs and attitudes, led to the emergence of 'cognitive' behaviour therapy.

The belief is that the patient, when faced with stressful situations, engages in unhelpful internal dialogues ('I don't think I am going to succeed').

In therapy these self-sabotaging internalised habits are replaced with a more constructive strategy: 'It's going to be difficult, it would be surprising if I wasn't going to feel a bit anxious. But provided I take things slowly and follow the plan I worked out in therapy, I can cope.'

One particular aspect is 'training in problem solving'. This is done through modelling, where the therapist shows the patient how to tackle certain problems while speaking his thoughts aloud. The emphasis is on reason, on dealing rationally with everyday problems.

The systemic approach: Advances in the disciplines of microphysics and electronics over the past 30 years have led to a new way of thinking about physical phenomena, and this has influenced the way in which social and psychological phenomena are conceptualised.

It became increasingly difficult to isolate and study individual phenomena, such as electrons, isolated pieces of behaviour, or individual pathology, as all these seemed to be part of the larger context within which they occurred. Interaction between two people, for instance, could not be sensibly studied by just observing one of the participants; nor could it be done by ignoring the circumstances of that interaction.

The systemic approach is not interested in the personal characteristics, unconscious mind, or the personal life history of each given individual. Instead it is concerned with the observable manifestations of interaction, between people in a given context, with all the verbal and non-verbal behaviour between people i.e. with 'communication'. It is implied that you cannot *not* communicate: even if A tries very hard not to communicate, by the very act of doing so A communicates that he doesn't want to communicate.

The systemic approach holds that 'everything is communication', including symptomatic behaviour and experiences.

At present the systemic approach is most frequently applied to the family. The family is viewed as a miniature social system which behaves as if it were a unit. This unit establishes over a period of time a kind of equilibrium, known as 'homeostasis': it is the tendency of the system to remain the same. When the homeostasis, this often delicate balance, threatens to be disturbed, all members will make efforts to maintain it. Such a disturbance can be caused by a death in the family, the arrival of a new child, unemployment, the move to another house and neighbourhood, etc.

If Emma, aged 9, is constantly tearful and her mother concerned about her,

... then father will be affected, not only by Emma but also by mother's worries about Emma, and her brother will also show reactions, which in turn will affect Emma, who may then change her behaviour, which will then have the effect of... etc., etc., ...

The systemic approach is concerned with the effects of behaviours upon behaviours, and of the effect of those behaviours on the original behaviours and so on. Interaction is a circle of events and effects.

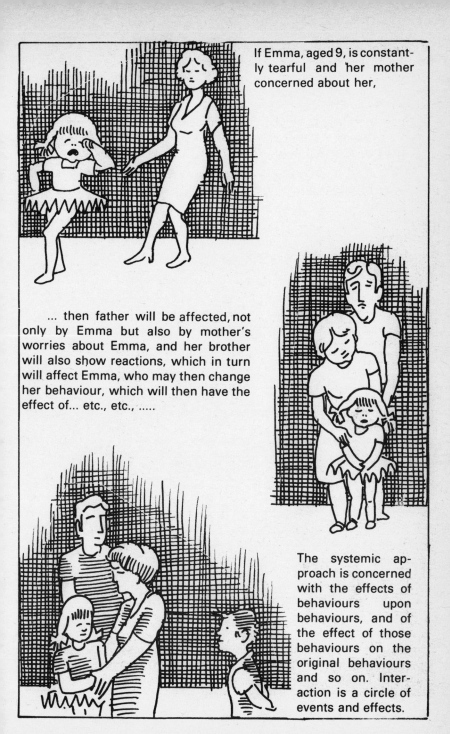

Let us assume that Emma's parents have marital problems. Over a period of time she develops what other people may call 'symptoms': she cannot sleep, she cries a lot, she doesn't want to go to school, she has frequent tummy aches.

Emma is the family member who is most obviously, certainly most visibly, affected by the marital problems. The parents' conflict threatens the family homeostasis and the girl's symptoms can be seen as an SOS about the family disturbance.

The symptoms are a message (communication) that she suffers pain as a result of having to cope with her parents' problems. At the same time, these symptoms can be seen as a kind of strategy, serving a function for the family — they have the effect of uniting the parents in their joint concern over the child's symptoms. The girl is caught: she may believe, consciously or unconsciously, that giving up her symptoms may lead to parental separation, but not giving them up will make her even more miserable. So miserable that her parents will take her to the doctor, in order that she can be treated. And the doctor may oblige. Emma has become the 'identified patient' in the family.

If Emma is referred on to a psychiatrist who uses the systemic approach things may be quite different. The family becomes the patient, the traditional definitions of who the patient is, and who is exhibiting symptoms are not accepted. The provisional diagnosis may establish Emma as her parents' 'failed marriage guidance counsellor' rather than as the sick member in an otherwise healthy family, or as the 'victim' of her parents' inability to face their own problems. In the systemic approach there is no room for victims and victimisers.

The aim of treatment is to change the structure of the system so that endless feedback circles are interrupted. This can be done in various ways.

In order to relieve Emma of her age-inappropriate responsibilities the therapist may decide to draw boundaries within the family and create a parental sub-system (mum and dad) and a sibling sub-system (Emma and her brother). This can be done by physically imposing a kind of barrier between children and parents in the session and thus releasing Emma from the position of go-between or in-between her parents. The therapist could at the same time encourage the parents to change their communication pattern (creating a spouse sub-system): 'See whether you can talk to your wife in such a way that she can reply to you calmly'. This approach is known as *structural*. The therapist is actively trying to change the family structure, i.e. the way that family members relate to and communicate with each other.

The *strategic* therapist also aims at eventually changing the family structure, but he goes about it in a different way. He tries to put the family in a bind with regard to their current interaction and hopes to create a situation where the family as a whole needs to find a new solution. This can be done, for instance, by paradoxically prescribing the symptomatic behaviour.

In the case of Emma, the therapist could say that her problems, distressing though they might be, also had a good side. Emma's problems make it possible for both parents to show what loving parents they are. This has had the effect of enabling her parents to postpone important discussions about their own relationship. ' Emma, you should continue having problems until such time that your parents let you know that they no longer need your help and that they are ready to discuss important issues in their life without having to involve you.'

Emma's initial presenting of symptomatic behaviour, which her parents saw as an illness, out of their daughter's control, has become redefined as a deliberate strategy to help the parents save their marriage.

Family therapists agree that this sort of intervention could be seen as a deliberate distortion of reality. They are not worried about the truth of their statements but rather about their usefulness. The main aim is 'to stop the dance' and this can often be achieved by presenting a different experience and perception of reality, however outrageous, so that a new way out of an impasse can be found by the family and its members.

Family therapy often addresses not only the people in the room but also the extended family — a 'supra-system'. Other supra-systems can be included in the systemic treatment process: school, other agencies such as social services, church, work sphere etc.

The boundaries of the initial system can be vastly extended and the systems psychiatrist might end up addressing the political supra-system of society as a whole, but would no longer then be at a 'meta-level' i.e. at a point 'outside' the system.

Most systems-oriented psychiatrists/therapists prefer to stay at the family level. They recognise the inter-relationship between family and wider social factors, but it is left to other groups of professionals to investigate the latter.

Social approaches

Some psychiatrists attempt to understand and treat mental disorder in relation to social factors. It is the social milieu which is seen to trigger off, reinforce or potentially combat the patient's disorder.

The social approach received its impetus from sociology. A few studies in the late 50's and early 60's in the USA and UK looked at the relationship between the occurrence of mental disorder (and in particular schizophrenia) and social class. This showed that underprivileged urban areas contained a disproportionate number of psychologically disturbed people: severe mental disorder was seen much more frequently in the lowest social classes as defined by income and housing. Why?

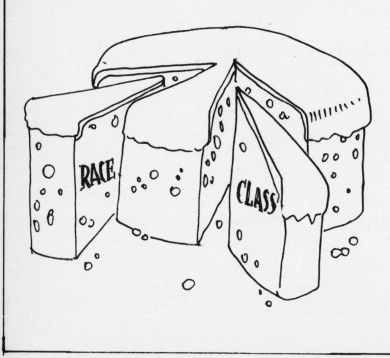

- ● Poor social circumstances and the stresses and strains of living in poverty drive people mad.
- ● Mad people drift towards poor areas as anywhere else they are unacceptable.
- ● Poor people put their mad friends or family members into public mental hospitals whereas richer people can afford private help and may therefore not appear in the statistics.

This work stimulated some psychiatrists to study in more detail how certain social factors influence a person's life. They looked at 'life events' which they regarded as a kind of 'social factor' possibly causing mental distress, e.g. moving house, starting school, graduations, exams, change of job, births and deaths in the family, adolescents leaving home, illness, redundancy.

Other psychiatrists concerned themselves with the effects of more general social conditions such as overcrowding, inflation, unemployment, competitiveness, consumerism, political repression, sexual inequality.

However, psychiatrists are not in a position to change these conditions, so the *practice* of social psychiatry draws many of its treatment approaches from other models, notably the psychodynamic and the behavioural.

For example, **group therapy** was an extension of the psychodynamic approach. A group could provide multiple 'transferences' between various group members and not just with the analyst.

These transferences could then be related more generally to the making and breaking of interpersonal relationships. But groups were also, on a more superficial level, regarded as good models for social situations: learning to confront openly and be confronted, to speak one's mind in public, to share worries and anxieties, to talk about relationship problems. And, in addition, groups were obviously cheaper, as a number of people could receive treatment at the same time.

A therapy group often consists of between eight and ten patients who meet once weekly for up to 90 minutes with one or two therapists. The group soon establishes its own rules which will be much influenced by the orientation of the therapist(s).

At one end of the spectrum there is psychodynamically-oriented group therapy. Here the therapist studies what happens between people in the group and tries to interpret this to the group as a whole, linking the group process with the personal contributions and experiences of the individual members.

This may then be related by individual members to their experiences and actions in other social groups, past and present, such as work, family or friends.

Another 'social' approach is the **therapeutic community**. Between 10 to 50 patients live together, either as day patients or in-patients, and try to understand their everyday interactions and conflicts. In contrast to the traditional mental hospital, the patients are encouraged to be active participants and collaborators in their own treatment and that of others. Self-regulation is emphasised rather than restraint (remember Tuke again — see pp.16-17) and the social organisation is an integral part of the treatment.

Four key concepts are: tolerance, democratisation, communalism and active rehabilitation.

At the other end of the spectrum are 'encounter' groups which are rarely used in public psychiatry. Their main aim is to remove certain constraints that are seen as inhibiting personal growth. The group demands frankness and the expression of what is normally held back.

Psychiatrists usually believe that these types of groups are potentially damaging to fragile individuals. Colourful things can happen in these groups.

Some community psychiatric services are currently being re-organised with a new emphasis on **crisis intervention**.

Mental problems constitute crises for the symptomatic sufferer (the 'identified patient') and his/her environment. Contrary to the common belief that crises are bad and should be eliminated quickly or defused through hospitalisation and medical treatment, a crisis intervention approach attempts to use crises positively. A crisis is a sign of and demand for change which is difficult to achieve, but the process of change can be initiated with the help of interventions by professionals who see their role as assisting the patient and his relatives or friends to overcome fears and other obstacles. Mobilising 'self help' potential is a major aim. Patients identified as disturbed and disturbing are seen in their own (home) environment and hospitalisation as a quick professional take-over is largely avoided. This approach does require the cooperation of other agencies and community resources.

If treatment or hospital admission is recommended by the crisis intervention team then this is always done in a way which does not go along with forcing one person into a 'sick role'.

Eclecticism

Most psychiatrists have a preference for one approach or another, due to their own personal experiences, beliefs, training, etc. But except in highly specialised units, it is in psychiatric practice very difficult to implement only one treatment approach in puristic form with every patient.

Even the most organic psychiatrist will occasionally use psychotherapy methods, and even the psychoanalyst will — if working in public psychiatry with very disturbed patients — at times have to resort to the use of drugs.

Most psychiatrists therefore think that for practical reasons they need to integrate the various approaches into their individual brand of eclecticism. At best this can lead to openness and flexibility. At worst it hides rigidity behind the mask of tolerance.

PSYCHIATRY IN ACTION

The four stages of psychiatric processing are: referral, diagnosis, treatment, follow-up.

The referral process (or 'how to become a patient')

Not everyone would think right away of referring a person to a psychiatrist if he/she behaves in a disturbed or disordered way. It will depend very much on the context within which the disturbed behaviour occurs as to what name it is given and who is going to deal with it.

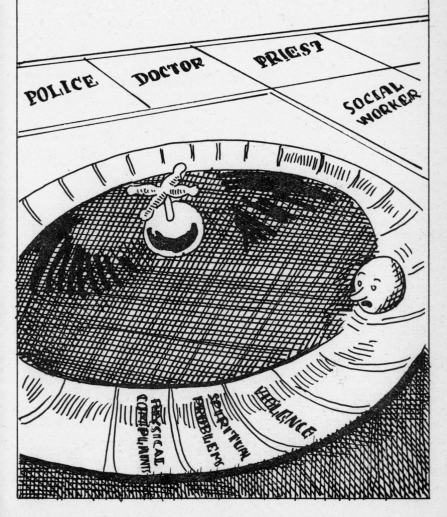

How does what may later be termed mental disorder manifest itself in the first place?

Some change needs to take place, inside the individual and perhaps also (sometimes only) in the environment. At a subjective level some of the most common changes are: a disturbance in thinking; apprehension about one's ability to control voluntarily one's thoughts and actions; acute anxiety; depression.

There are a number of ways in which change can be experienced and responded to.

1. The subjective change is not regarded as a problem by the affected person but disturbs others.

Example:

A is in extremely high spirits, he buys three cars at the same time, gives a lot of money to people he happens to meet on the street, talks all the time, does not sleep, etc.

A himself isn't apparently very aware of change; he may just feel a better person, whereas others think that he is damaging himself, and psychiatric referral comes about to stop him ruining himself, or his relatives, physically and financially.

2. The person himself is aware of subjective change, and sees it as a problem, but does not look for a remedy or help.

Example:

' I deserve to be ill, I must die, my bowels are rotting, nobody can do anything about it, I'm just a problem for everybody else, others should be protected from me.'

This is disturbing to others and they want to get help for the suffering person for humanitarian reasons, but also often because it is unbearable to be exposed to this type of experience.

3. The person regards his/her change as a problem and seeks help. Others agree and respond.

Example:

' I'm depressed — can I see a psychiatrist?'

' Thank God — I've noticed for some time. Why don't you go to your doctor and ask him to put you on to a psychiatrist.'

4. The person regards his/her change as a problem and seeks help but others take a different stand.

Example:

'I'm depressed — can I see a psychiatrist?'

'You should pull your socks up and get your finger out, not waste time talking to a trick cyclist!'

Whether a referral to a psychiatrist is actually to happen also depends on a number of factors: the availability of psychiatric services, their quality, the opinion the referrer has of them (most referrals come about via the family doctor) the degree of urgency, etc.

The diagnostic process

The *patient* who is about to see a psychiatrist for the first time may have all sorts of fears and hopes, depending on his general state of mind, his imagination, what other people might have told him about psychiatrists, and how much he has been pushed to go.

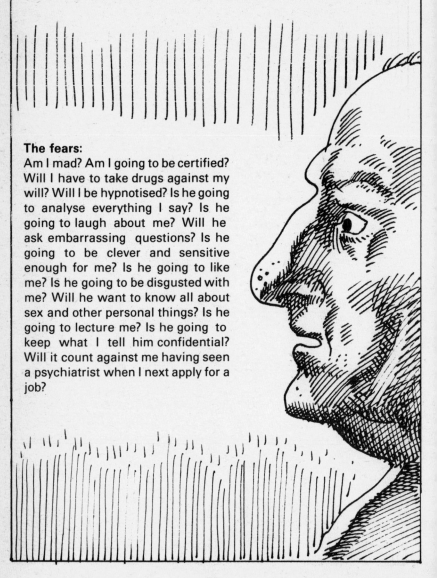

The fears:

Am I mad? Am I going to be certified? Will I have to take drugs against my will? Will I be hypnotised? Is he going to analyse everything I say? Is he going to laugh about me? Will he ask embarrassing questions? Is he going to be clever and sensitive enough for me? Is he going to like me? Is he going to be disgusted with me? Will he want to know all about sex and other personal things? Is he going to lecture me? Is he going to keep what I tell him confidential? Will it count against me having seen a psychiatrist when I next apply for a job?

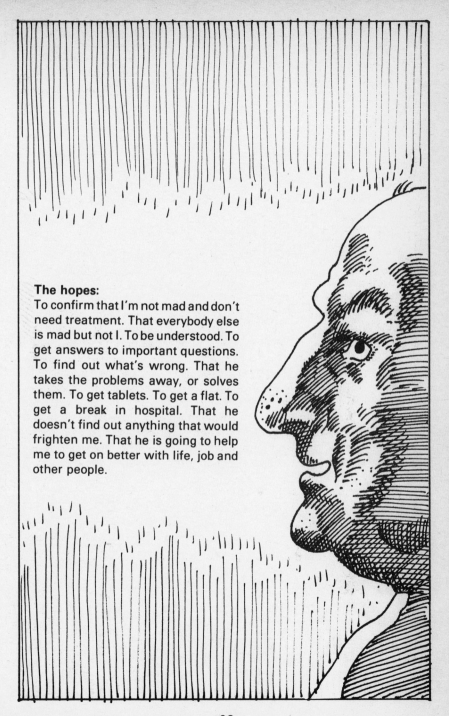

The hopes:
To confirm that I'm not mad and don't need treatment. That everybody else is mad but not I. To be understood. To get answers to important questions. To find out what's wrong. That he takes the problems away, or solves them. To get tablets. To get a flat. To get a break in hospital. That he doesn't find out anything that would frighten me. That he is going to help me to get on better with life, job and other people.

And what goes on in the *psychiatrist* before he sees the patient? He will probably have much more experience seeing patients than patients have seeing psychiatrists — his hopes and fears are therefore less intense, or at least less conscious.

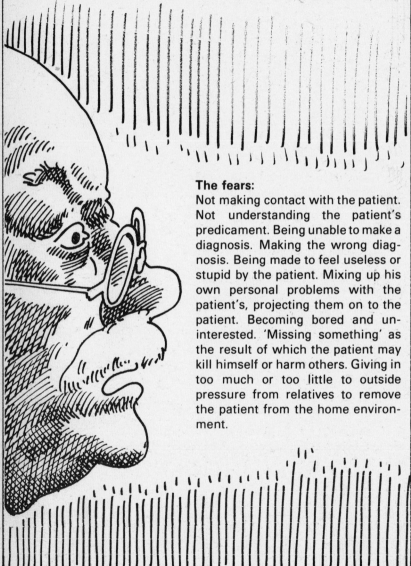

The fears:
Not making contact with the patient. Not understanding the patient's predicament. Being unable to make a diagnosis. Making the wrong diagnosis. Being made to feel useless or stupid by the patient. Mixing up his own personal problems with the patient's, projecting them on to the patient. Becoming bored and uninterested. 'Missing something' as the result of which the patient may kill himself or harm others. Giving in too much or too little to outside pressure from relatives to remove the patient from the home environment.

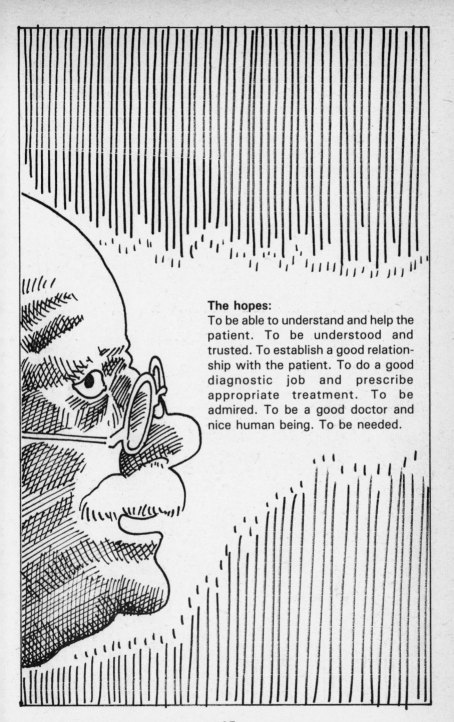

The hopes:
To be able to understand and help the patient. To be understood and trusted. To establish a good relationship with the patient. To do a good diagnostic job and prescribe appropriate treatment. To be admired. To be a good doctor and nice human being. To be needed.

Whatever the hopes and fears, the aim of the first encounter is assessment: the psychiatrist assesses the patient and the patient assesses the psychiatrist. More specifically, the psychiatrist aims at establishing a preliminary diagnosis and possibly a treatment plan.

The patient, on the other hand, assesses whether psychiatry in general and that psychiatrist in particular have anything to offer him.

How this mutual assessment takes place depends on the psychiatrist's approach and the patient's frame of mind.

The psychiatrist's approach: As we have seen, theoretical frameworks and styles vary considerably. The organic psychiatrist will focus on observable symptoms, on what is 'abnormal'.

A psychodynamically-orientated colleague, however, may encourage the patient to say anything that comes to mind, thereby expressing interest in whatever the patient regards as important, whether it relates superficially to symptoms or not. The inexperienced psychiatrist of whatever orientation may go through an endless checklist of questions, justifying the claim that a psychiatrist is a person who has a question for every answer.

The patient's frame of mind: Some patients are what psychiatrists call 'co-operative'. But other patients unwittingly try to sabotage the assessment out of fear of what it would feel like to face and deal with the problem, or to change, no matter how much they rationally want to ('The devil I know is much better and less dangerous than the one I don't').

The psychiatrist's main aim in the initial assessment interview is to get answers to the following questions:

What sort of person is the patient? Why has he/she come to see a psychiatrist? Why now? How is she/he socially, emotionally and intellectually functioning at the moment? Is there anything wrong with the patient? And if so, what? Is treatment needed?

To answer these very broad questions he needs to give some direction to the interview. For his own convenience the assessment will focus on four areas — so that a fairly comprehensive picture of the patient can be obtained in a systematic fashion:

The presenting symptoms
'What has brought you here?' or 'What seems to be the problem?' (and variations on this theme). Onset and circumstances of symptoms: who first noticed them; their course — how they developed and changed over time; accurate description of what they are like now.

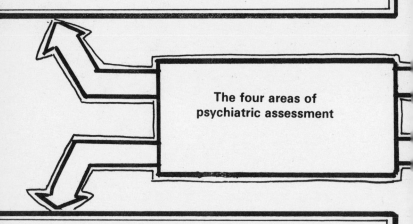

The four areas of psychiatric assessment

The personal history
Birth, infancy, childhood, adolescence. Development delays (speech, movement, toilet training), early relationships with sibs and adults, schooling and further education, 'social performance' and sexual 'adjustment'. A brief assessment of the 'pre-morbid personality': the way the person functioned prior to occurrence of symptoms.

The family history
The patient's family background, grandparents, parents, siblings and other important relatives, their lives, occupations, important events. Any problems — mental, social or physical (in order to establish social or genetic transmission of disorder).

The mental state examination
General behaviour and appearance.
Speech and talk.
Mood and emotions.
Perception.
Thought processes.
Cognition.
Self-evaluation.

The patient may well wonder why on earth the psychiatrist wants to know all the details of the presenting symptoms, family and personal history — some seemingly irrelevant to why he/she has come to see the psychiatrist. But she/he will be even more surprised when the *mental state examination* takes place. The psychiatrist probes various areas of psychological functioning with very specific questions.

To the psychiatrist they have the function of evaluating the patient's mind for qualitative deviations from a norm which is set by the psychiatrist (or his theories). To the patient some of these questions may seem quite straightforward, others quite obscure.

Examples of straight questions:
Do you ever feel low? Do you ever feel like hitting someone? Do you feel that you have changed in any way? How many children does the Queen have and what are their names?

Examples of less straight questions:

Do people seem to drop hints? Do you feel that they are talking behind your back or that strange things are happening around you? Do you hear voices when nobody is around? Do you ever feel you are another person, a famous one, or some kind of robot without a will of your own, without feelings? Are you made to do things that you don't want to do? Are you singled out for something you don't understand?

However irrelevant or obscure they may seem, these and other questions aim at assessing various aspects of the patient's mind, which is sub-divided into six different parts.

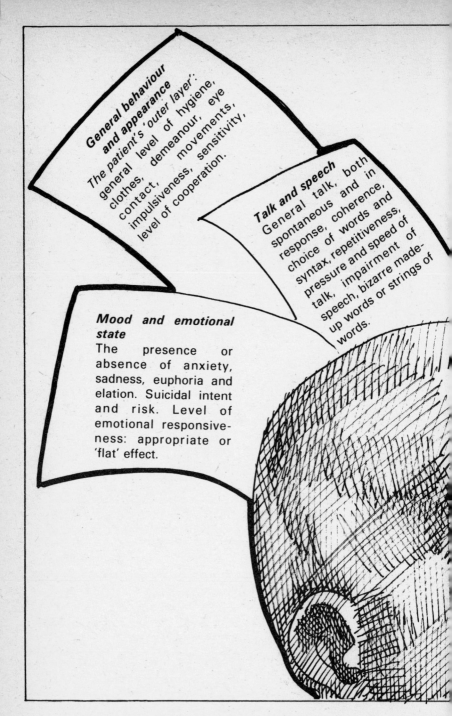

General behaviour and appearance

The patient's 'outer layer': general level of hygiene, clothes, demeanour, eye contact, movements, impulsiveness, sensitivity, level of cooperation.

Talk and speech

General talk, both spontaneous and in response, coherence, choice of words and syntax, repetitiveness, pressure and speed of talk, impairment of speech, bizarre made-up words or strings of words.

Mood and emotional state

The presence or absence of anxiety, sadness, euphoria and elation. Suicidal intent and risk. Level of emotional responsiveness: appropriate or 'flat' effect.

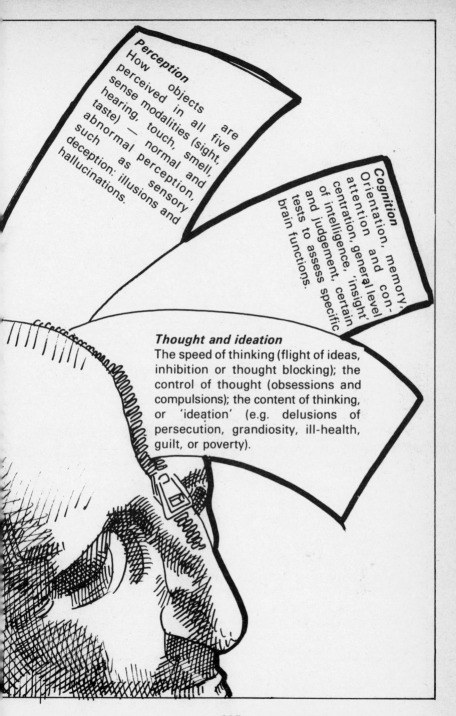

Perception
How objects are perceived in all five sense modalities (sight, hearing, touch, smell, taste) — normal and abnormal perception, such as sensory deception: illusions and hallucinations.

Cognition
Orientation, memory, attention and concentration, general level of intelligence, 'insight' and judgement, certain tests to assess specific brain functions.

Thought and ideation
The speed of thinking (flight of ideas, inhibition or thought blocking); the control of thought (obsessions and compulsions); the content of thinking, or 'ideation' (e.g. delusions of persecution, grandiosity, ill-health, guilt, or poverty).

This subdivision of the mind into separate areas of mental functioning is somewhat arbitrary — the various parts are of course interrelated. Mood affects thought, thought affects perception, which in turn affects and is affected by cognition, and so on.

But for diagnostic purposes, psychiatrists find it helpful to assess the various functions of the mind separately.
There is plenty of information — but how is the psychiatrist going to put it all together?
Psychiatrists have, very broadly speaking, five diagnostic choices:

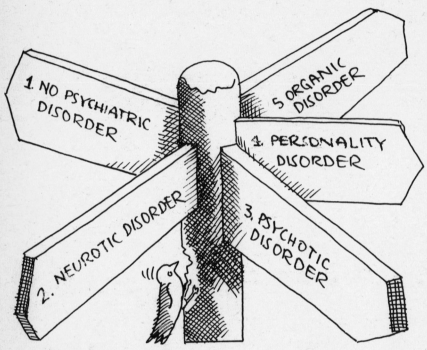

1. No psychiatric disorder

Many patients will be pleased about this diagnosis. But might it simply mean that there was no way in which the psychiatrist could fit the symptoms into any of the existing categories of mental disorder?

What if the patient insists that there is 'something wrong with me'? Is it a sign of mental disorder to insist on mental disorder despite contradictory statements by the psychiatrist?

Psychiatrist:

"Yes, there is something wrong with you, namely that you insist that there is something wrong with you when there is nothing wrong with you."

2. Neurotic disorder

The point where normality ends and neurosis starts is often hard to identify. Psychiatrists have tried to define the term neurosis more clearly.

They have not come to any agreement other than that neurosis is a disorder which is not physical in nature but psychological. The patient suffering from a neurosis usually knows about it but cannot do much about it. The symptoms appear irrational to the patient:

'I know it's crazy but I cannot help thinking this.'

This is what psychiatrists call 'insight' — the patient is only too aware of the disturbance in mental functioning.

Psychiatrists regard a person suffering from a neurotic disorder as in need of treatment only if there is considerable personal discomfort or subjective misery, if the patient's capacity for work is disturbed, or if he is unable to establish or maintain personal relationships.

Neurotic disorder is the most frequent diagnosis made in psychiatry. Each psychiatric approach has its own theory as to the etiology of neurosis: psychodynamic psychiatrists see it as a manifestation of unresolved conflicts, behaviourists interpret it as the result of maladaptive learning, systems psychiatrists as a strategy to maintain homeostasis, and their more organically-minded colleagues may blame in part certain genetic and constitutional factors.

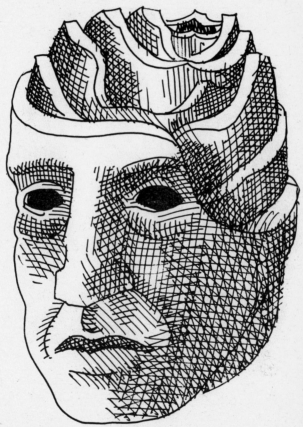

Most psychiatrists, whatever their approach, say that neuroses can present quite different clinical pictures, and they differentiate between several forms of neurosis.

Anxiety neurosis

Anxiety is the main feature: fear, dread, alarm, the feeling of impending danger. The observable physical symptoms include palpitation, sweating, restlessness, breathlessness, muscle tension, trembling, chest pain, faintness, fast pulse, frequent toileting.

An acute panic state can occur with devastating suddenness, a chronic anxiety state may last for years.

Hysteria

Anxiety is converted (transformed) into a physical dysfunction which is 'real' to the patient and 'objectively observable' to the doctor. But physical examination can give no medical explanation for the symptoms, such as blindness, paralysis, deafness, speech disorder, tremor or memory loss.

Convulsions such as those described by Charcot are nowadays very rare: the symptoms have become more subtle and often mimic neurological disorders (e.g. multiple sclerosis).

The patient does not usually know that his mind is producing these symptoms.

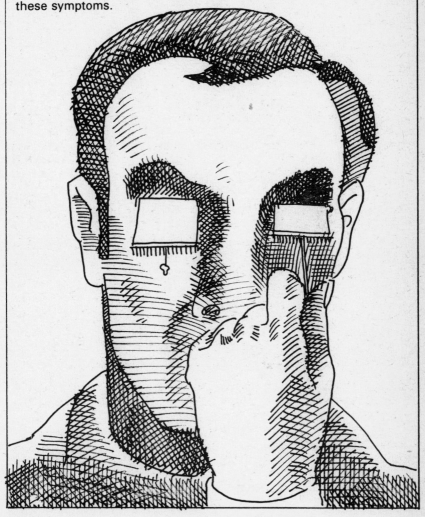

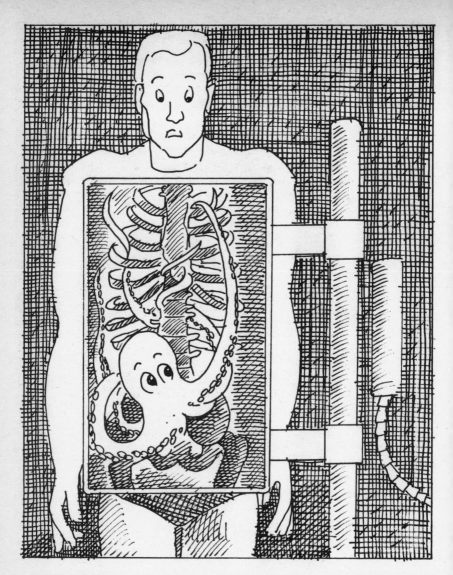

Hypochondriasis
Persistent anxious preoccupation with physical health. 'I know you will think it's crazy, but I have this headache and I'm sure it's a brain tumour, well, at least it could be. And I couldn't go to the toilet for two days, perhaps it's spreading to the bowels, I know it's a stupid idea, but it could happen — I always think of the worst...'

Phobic neurosis

A phobia is an irrational fear of a specific object or situation: aeroplanes, streets, open spaces, enclosed places, all sorts of objects — rats, cats, knives, what-have-you. These objects or situations arouse in the patient severe anxiety or panic. The patient does almost anything to avoid the phobia-related objects or situations.

Obsessional neurosis

Obsessions are repetitive thougths or images which force themselves onto the patient's mind. Although he recognises them as 'senseless' and 'a nuisance', he cannot stop them from coming to his mind, he cannot forget them. When these thoughts are put into action one speaks of a compulsion.

Thought: 'There are germs everywhere.'

Action: Not touching anything, blowing air away from mouth continuously. Obsessions and compulsions mostly centre around dirt, sex, death and cruelty.

Neurotic depression

Feelings of depression are of course an everyday experience for many people who are not in the psychiatric sense 'ill'. Here, though, they are of disabling intensity.

'I'm fed up with life, this town is depressing, I cannot enjoy anything, don't want to see anybody (cries), I wish I were dead, I can't sleep, can't eat...'

Psychosomatic illness

This concept short-circuits the seemingly unresolvable question of where the body ends and the mind begins. It is defined as a disease in which emotional disturbance plays an important part in causing, aggravating or maintaining the physical symptoms. Examples are asthma, ulcers, certain skin diseases, intestinal bleeding, and some forms of juvenile diabetes.

3. Psychotic disorder

If patients have 'insight' into the madness of their madness, they may be called 'neurotic'. If, however, they do not have this kind of insight, if they do not regard their beliefs or thoughts as irrational or absurd when they appear to be so to others, then they may be diagnosed as 'out of touch with reality', or in short: psychotic.

The difference between psychotics and neurotics is said to be that: *'Neurotics build castles in the air, while psychotics live in them.'*

The psychotic person lives in a world which has its own logic and rules (and often its own language). A world which appears to be inaccessible to others, incomprehensible, non-sensical, meaningless.

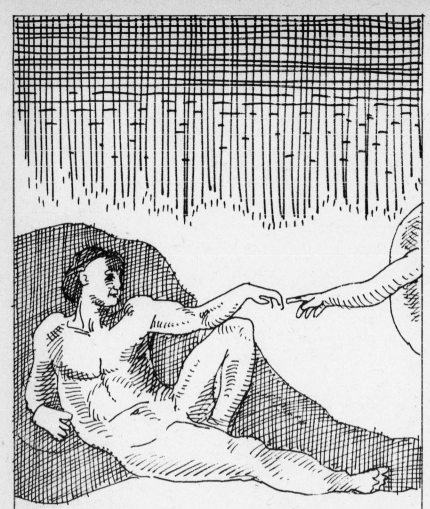

'Everything that happens is in reference to me..... I know very well that this tendency to relate everything to oneself, to bring everything that happens into connection with one's own person, is a common phenomenon among mental patients. But in my case the very reverse is true. Since God entered into nerve-contact with me exclusively, I became in a way for God the only human being, or simply the human being around whom everything turns, to whom everything that happens must be related and who therefore, from his own point of view, must also relate all things to himself.'
(**Memoirs of My Nervous Illness,** by Judge Schreber.)

In contemporary psychiatry the term psychosis is used for severe mental disorders in which delusions and hallucinations are the main features.

A *delusion* is a false unshakeable belief which is out of keeping with the patient's social and cultural background, and inaccessible to accepted reasoning.

Schreber's belief that God is in nerve-contact with him exclusively is one example of a delusion. It cannot be challenged.

A *hallucination* is a false perception: the person perceives something that is not really there. All sense modalities can be affected: auditory (e.g. hearing voices), visual (seeing people), olfactory (nasty smells), tactile (being touched) and gustatory (strange tastes).

'They are putting hot needles in my stomach, they suck my brain out, my heart is transplanted – faster heart beat.. taken away.. there are good voices in my right ear and bad ones in my left.. the food tastes of arsenic..'

Behavioural disorders are often present: tic-like grimacing, stuporous catatonic behaviour (muteness, odd postures held for hours), 'automatic obedience', negativism (the patient always does the opposite of what he is being asked).

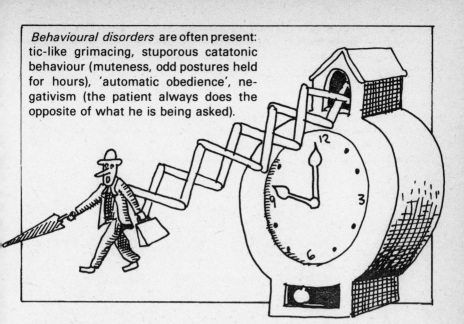

Also *affective disorders* i.e. disturbances of emotional response: apathy, emotional blunting and shallowness, incongruous or inappropriate responses.

Another prominent feature of psychosis is 'thought disorder', seen in the use of language: incoherence, 'word salads', neologisms (invention of new words), excessive mannerisms, verbigeration (senseless repetition over many days of the same words or phrases), stilted phrasing.

Sample:

'Mental health is wealth. Cain fell Lucifer prostitute, grownshitup-bumber, for the Creation understands Germany in Voice New Order, kiss your cunt have. No hard on feelings.'

The paintings of psychotics are often the visible images of seemingly disjointed thinking and experiencing.

Non-sensical as the behaviour and communications of psychotics may appear at first sight, there are psychiatrists who have tried to make sense of them, to render them intelligible. Notably R.D. Laing, and some of his co-workers and followers (sometimes referred to as 'anti-psychiatrists') have shown that psychotics' symptoms can sometimes be seen as comprehensible responses to the situations which they feel themselves to be in. Psychosis can also be seen as a strategy adopted by a person to deal with relationships made impossible by the contradictory demands of others.

There are four major categories of psychosis.

Schizophrenia

Kraepelin described and named the condition of 'dementia praecox'. It was renamed by the Swiss psychiatrist E. Bleuler as 'schizophrenia'. Kraepelin and Bleuler did not 'discover' schizophrenia — they 'invented' it. It is only a concept by which a variety of symptoms (and the people exhibiting these symptoms) are grouped together.

Yet, though schizophrenia is only a concept and a methodological convenience, most psychiatrists treat schizophrenia as if it were a well-defined illness, despite the fact that nobody knows what it really is, let alone what causes it.

A diagnosis of schizophrenia is now made if the following clinical features are present and if there are no known physical causes: certain kinds of 'passivity' experiences, such as feelings that one's thoughts are being broadcast, stolen or forced upon one.

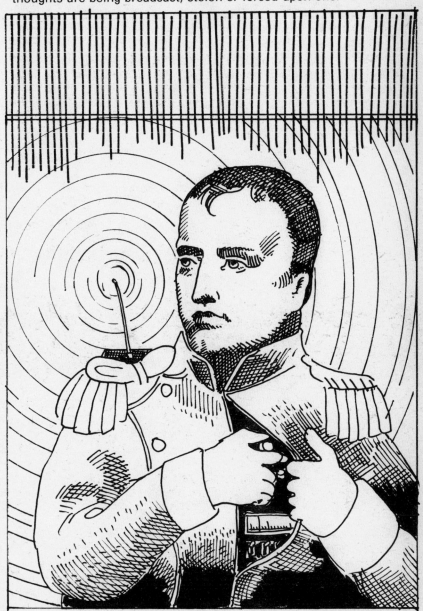

Affective psychosis

A psychosis with a morbid change of mood in the form of either depression or its opposite mania, or, in manic-depressive psychosis, alternations between the two.

Many psychiatrists, and particularly those of organic orientation, believe MDP to be a well-defined illness: it comes and goes in cycles. During a manic episode the patient shows a mixture of elation, constant talking and increased activity, rapid succession of ideas and grandiose delusions.

'I feel so close to God, so inspired by His spirit that in a sense I am God. I see the future, plan the Universe, save mankind; I am utterly and completely immortal; I am even male and female. The whole Universe, all nature and life, all spirits are cooperating and connected with me. All things are possible. I am identical with all spirits from God to Satan. I reconcile Good and Evil and create light, darkness, worlds, universes......'

Psychiatrists note that mania does not last for a long time and that it is followed either by a spell of normality or a depressive phase.

This depressive phase may be extremely severe, with the patient being almost immobile, refusing to eat and talk and it may last for many months. This may then again be followed by a manic or hypomanic (less severe) episode, and so on.

Often a manic episode never takes place and some psychiatrists then call this a unipolar manic-depressive psychosis — as opposed to the bipolar one with regular swings.

Paranoid psychosis

Some of the patients who cannot be fitted into any of the schizophrenia categories find themselves here. There is usually a circumscribed delusional system present, but hallucination is not necessary for a diagnosis of paranoid psychosis.

Organic psychosis

Organic disorders (see next page) can present with the picture of psychosis.

The treatment of any of these four broad categories of psychotic disorders depends — as always — on the individual psychiatrist's approach.

Most psychiatrists, though, will at one point or another, feel the need to resort to drugs — not because they necessarily believe that this will cure the psychosis, but in order to control the most florid and disturbing symptoms. The intensity and suffering can be unbearable, not only for the patient, but also for the psychiatrist. Sharing the experiences of a psychotic can threaten a psychiatrist's own mental balance.

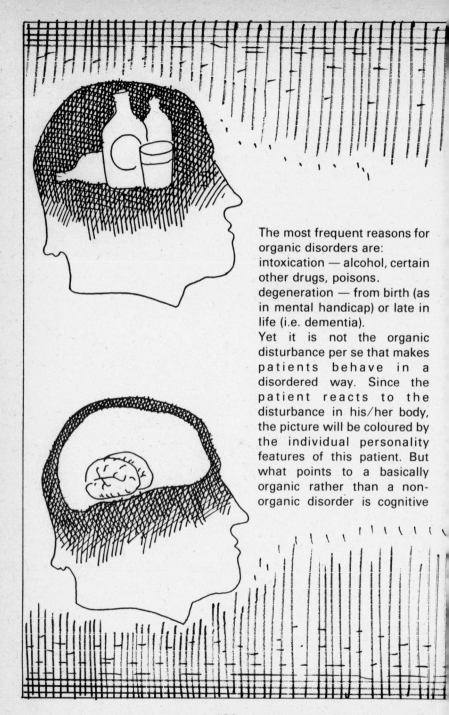

The most frequent reasons for organic disorders are:
intoxication — alcohol, certain other drugs, poisons.
degeneration — from birth (as in mental handicap) or late in life (i.e. dementia).
Yet it is not the organic disturbance per se that makes patients behave in a disordered way. Since the patient reacts to the disturbance in his/her body, the picture will be coloured by the individual personality features of this patient. But what points to a basically organic rather than a non-organic disorder is cognitive

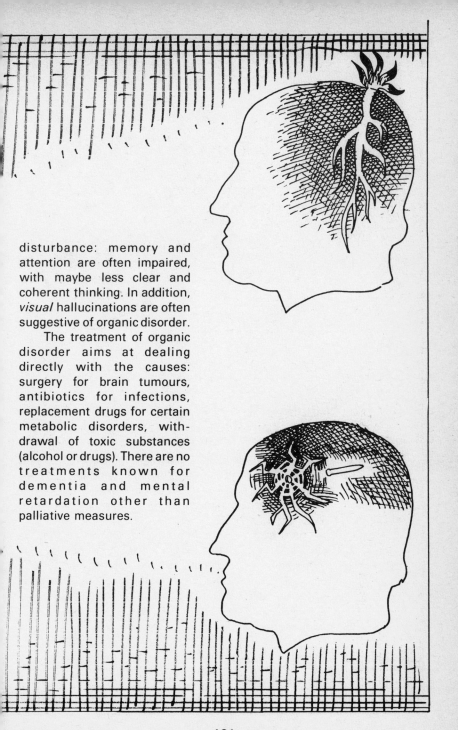

disturbance: memory and attention are often impaired, with maybe less clear and coherent thinking. In addition, *visual* hallucinations are often suggestive of organic disorder.

The treatment of organic disorder aims at dealing directly with the causes: surgery for brain tumours, antibiotics for infections, replacement drugs for certain metabolic disorders, withdrawal of toxic substances (alcohol or drugs). There are no treatments known for dementia and mental retardation other than palliative measures.

5. Personality disorder

Psychiatrists attempt to discriminate between mental illness and abnormal personality. Illness is seen as a syndrome which disrupts the normal continuity of the personality: once the illness subsides the 'real' personality shows again and can then be assessed as to its normality.

The central feature of personality disorder is some persistent degree of abnormality of character which is frequently, but not necessarily, anti-social in its manifestations. Some say that a personality disordered person, or 'psychopath', does what others would like to do if they didn't feel compelled to be 'civilised' — e.g. cheat, be aggressive, egocentric, impulsive, etc.

Contemporary psychiatry distinguishes between various degrees of personality disorder:

mild   **moderate**   **severe**

While there may be some hope of changing the ways of those with mild and moderate disorders, the severe cases or 'sociopaths' are often regarded as unchangeable.

The sociopath is thought of as having a serious defect of feeling, as 'affectionless', destructive, impulsive and seriously irresponsible.

Some psychiatrists refuse to make a diagnosis of psychopathy or sociopathy because such diagnoses imply rejection of the patient: that's the way the patient 'is' and one cannot therefore do much about it. However, most psychiatrists stick to the concept of personality disorder, but find it difficult to treat those so diagnosed because of their failure to respond to treatment.

'Treatment' therefore often consists of custodial care, or no treatment at all.

These five broad diagnostic categories and their various sub-groups provide a framework within which the specific diagnosis of the referred patient can be made. But there is some disagreement between psychiatrists not only about the accuracy of this kind of classification scheme, but about *the value of diagnosis* altogether.

Pro diagnosis:

1. Naming certain conditions is the basis for a common language among psychiatrists.

2. It is important to abstract from the individual case and look at the more general features of his/her disorder. This is the only way of finding out about common features of various disorders, and subsequently also common causes and treatments. Diagnoses group together these common features.

3. With firmly established diagnoses it is possible to compare the incidence of the same condition in different populations (e.g. industrial town vs rural village; village in Germany vs village in Sumatra) and thus draw inferences about the relative influence of socio-cultural and biological factors on the incidence of mental disorder.

4. In order to plan psychiatric services one needs to know the amount and degree of mental disorder ('psychiatric morbidity') within a specific community. Mental disorder can best be identified and quantified within a framework of diagnostic classifications.

***Contra* diagnosis:**

● Few patients fit neatly into textbook categories — each patient is unique. Making a diagnosis does not provide any new information about the individual so diagnosed — it just glosses over the complexity of the person's make-up.

● Labelling creates a spurious impression of understanding, and encourages the naïve assumption that mental disorders are clear-cut disease entities.

● The allocation of a particular cluster of symptoms to a specific diagnosis is to some degree an arbitrary process — some people diagnose schizophrenia where others diagnose manic-depressive psychosis. The diagnosis of schizophrenia, for instance, is far more frequently made by American psychiatrists than by their British colleagues. This is not evidence for the view that schizophrenia is more common in the US than in Britain, but simply shows that psychiatric illnesses are not entities which simply have to be observed in order to be classified, but are matters of definition.

● There is the temptation to view all sorts of behaviours as 'confirmation of the diagnosis' rather than to explore what other meanings they may have.

● The act of assigning a diagnosis necessarily focuses attention on patients' deficiencies rather than their assets.

● Many psychiatric diagnoses have perjorative connotations and often influence other people's behaviour towards patients, and patients' own attitudes towards themselves in unhelpful ways. Some phenomena of mental disorder are produced and/or maintained by the expectations created in patients and their environments by this labelling process.

The treatment process

The initial diagnosis affects the decision as to what is going to happen to the patient. There are a number of possibilities:

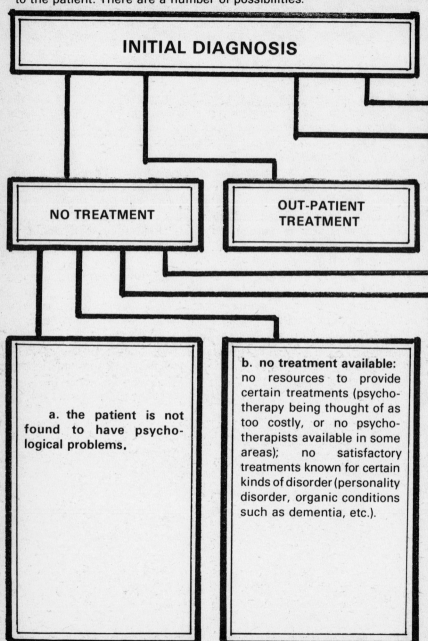

INITIAL DIAGNOSIS

NO TREATMENT

OUT-PATIENT TREATMENT

a. the patient is not found to have psychological problems.

b. no treatment available: no resources to provide certain treatments (psychotherapy being thought of as too costly, or no psychotherapists available in some areas); no satisfactory treatments known for certain kinds of disorder (personality disorder, organic conditions such as dementia, etc.).

136

IN-PATIENT TREATMENT	REFERRAL TO OTHER AGENCY

c. no treatment advisable: because treatment would make a person 'psychiatric', e.g. to treat the person who is 'clinically' depressed because he is unemployed lets politicians off the hook: the politically radical 'no treatment' option. Therapeutic nihilism: no treatment is a treatment in itself — it is therapeutic not to be dependent on psychiatry and psychiatrists. Particularly therapeutic with 'professional patients' — those addicted to psychiatric services.

d. no treatment necessary: it is hoped that the patient's symptoms will show 'spontaneous remission' i.e. will clear up without treatment, perhaps when the patient's circumstances change, if that is possible.

Out-patient treatment

Most psychiatric patients are out-patients: they come to see their psychiatrist anything from once weekly to once monthly or even less often, for an average time of about ten minutes.

In public psychiatry the patient has little choice as to which psychiatrist he sees and usually no say as to which treatment approach is used. He may or may not like a particular treatment method (the organic approach dominates public psychiatry); he may or may not like his psychiatrist as a person.

The *patient* soon finds himself in a very familiar social situation: the child wanting something from a parent, a citizen wanting something from the authorities, the outsider wanting something from the establishment. The patient might want to create this kind of role against the psychiatrist's efforts to get away from such a situation; or he might find a psychiatrist willing to play this game; or the patient might be forced into such a role by an authoritarian psychiatrist; but also the patient might find an ally in the psychiatrist in his attempt to face the complexity of life without having to resort to stereotyped roles and situations. However, it is very difficult not to get stuck in stereotyped role behaviour because of the very nature of the relationship between patient and psychiatrist. The patient sees the psychiatrist about a problem and asks the psychiatrist for help. He sees the psychiatrist as a professional rather than a friend.

This creates an imbalance from which psychiatrists often wish to escape. Similarly some patients feel uncomfortable about it and start asking questions about the personal life of their psychiatrist. Most psychiatrists say that to answer these types of questions would distract from the real task, that of helping the patient with his personal problems.

Psychiatrists may even go as far as to imply that the patient's curiosity is a defensive manoeuvre designed to avoid confronting his own difficulties.

Most patients go and see their psychiatrists regularly no matter what they deep down think about them. To the outsider such out-patient attendances seem like meaningless rituals, and patients themselves may look at these visits as something like going to the hairdresser, or having a social talk with the milkman.

To many patients the psychiatrist is no more than someone who listens, someone whom one can talk to, or just someone who is always 'there'.

This is why sometimes patients prolong their symptoms so as not to lose that constant figure — if they improve too rapidly they risk discharge. But there is also another fear: if one doesn't get better at all — is the psychiatrist going to get fed up?

The relationship between patient and psychiatrist can be seen as one of mutual influence. The *psychiatrist* is in part controlled by the patient's fluctuating mental state. For instance, if the patient shows or threatens destructive behaviour the psychiatrist cannot help responding in one way or another. Psychiatrists often experience this as being forced into action by their patients, as destructive behaviour may have legal consequences — both for the patient and the psychiatrist who can be sued for negligence.

　　'I'm so suicidal, if you don't admit me to hospital I'll throw myself under the next car – outside this hospital.'
Psychiatrists often feel anxious, depressed, useless and stupid when they feel manipulated or coerced by their patients.

141

Psychiatrists cannot choose whom they wish to treat but have to respond to demand and provide a service. The average psychiatrist therefore gets stuck with his patient as often as the patient with his psychiatrist. Only it is much more difficult for the psychiatrist to say so. His patient can tell him that he hates him or thinks he is stupid — and this sort of outburst may be regarded as a 'therapeutic expression of aggression'.

But the psychiatrist cannot usually afford to do the same, though he may have extremely hostile feelings towards some of his patients.

Psychiatrists therefore find themselves in a bind: they are supposed to be nice to their patients whilst resenting them and they may also demand of themselves to be 'genuine' and 'honest'.

Conversely, if a psychiatrist likes one of his patients a bit too much or falls in love with him/her, he is not allowed to show it under any circumstances and tends to feel extremely guilty; he may even have to consult a psychiatrist.

The patient on the other hand may be openly encouraged to express loving feelings and to fantasise about the psychiatrist.

Most psychiatrists would say that they don't mind suppressing certain feelings during their work. But it is tough to deal day-in, day-out with people who suffer, having to face questions in an area where doubt is the only thing that is certain, being exposed to hypersensitive people, having to deal with disorder and chaos.

Psychiatrists therefore often feel the need to protect themselves, whether this is with a white coat, a detached, allegedly 'scientific' approach, or by some other means.

Psychiatrists are under pressure: there is the expectation for them to do something, to have answers and solutions. Patients sometimes pressurise psychiatrists into giving advice although they have no advice to give, or into giving a prescription just in order to be seen 'doing something'. They may find themselves prescribing drugs against their better judgement, but will justify it by pointing out that the *patient* asked for it, and that there was simply no time to argue otherwise.

And psychiatrists are also under pressure from their psychiatric and medical colleagues who question the value of a certain method or the general approach, and who point at 'failures' and so on.

Psychiatrists need to see some of their patients get better — they need the occasional success to keep them going on with an often hopeless job. Sometimes they keep special 'pet' patients whom it seems they have helped: these patients are the living proof of their therapeutic skill and psychiatrists may find it almost as difficult to separate from these patients as vice versa.

In-patient treatment
There are different modes of admission to an in-patient ward: voluntary, compulsory and a mixture of the two.

Voluntary admission: the patient agrees that he/she should be an in-patient. Patients in this category can discharge themselves, even 'against medical advice'. But once in hospital the patient takes a risk: the psychiatrists may change his or her status from voluntary to compulsory or involuntary.

Compulsory admission: the patient is admitted to a mental hospital (or is kept there) against his or her own will. The ways in which compulsory admissions are instituted vary from country to country. But in principle, at least one person representing the medical profession, and one person representing the patient (family member, social worker or other) need to agree that the patient is suffering from mental illness or disorder and that he is a danger either to himself or to others.

Involuntary voluntary admission: the patient is 'persuaded' to become an in-patient:
verbally: 'If you don't go in voluntarily I'll section you.'
chemically: a major tranquilliser may be given by injection to calm the patient down and provide him with 'insight'.
physically: with the threat of physical force if the patient does not comply.

The patient's first impression of the in-patient section of a large psychiatric hospital:

Ugly building, endless corridors populated with patients who walk like robots (Is it their madness? Is it the drugs they get? Is it living in a bin?), staff in uniforms, behaving like prison guards, waving their long keys, screams from some rooms (Is it madness? Is it staff punishing patients?), mad-looking patients, grimaces, large dormitories, some windows with bars, doors that are locked, toilet doors that cannot be locked, resigned faces.

The prison-like admission procedure: personal data, certain formalities, possessions are registered, receipts given, 'dangerous objécts' (all a matter of definition) are removed.

The patient feels infantilised, a second-class citizen, a case, puzzled, confused, perplexed, horrified, amused, alienated.

And/or: happy to be looked after, to be safe, to be contained, to be able not to think, to sleep, not having to work, not having to be with family.

Impressions and observations over next few days: there are obvious favourites — patients whom staff are particularly fond of. Also there are patients who cause trouble, who rebel and who are then being shut up. There can be violence: patients vs patients, patients vs staff, staff vs patients. No obvious violence between staff and staff, but plenty of tension. Particularly between different shifts: they do different things. Hierarchies among nurses. Nice nurses and harsh ones. They write reports about patients, observe them, watch them all the time. They discuss patients among themselves.

Spend the day 'productively' in occupational therapy department: here all sorts of things are offered, from art (therapy) to industrial work, to basket-making, making buttons and licking stamps. Certain games in leisure time, e.g. bingo. General understimulation.

Other ward routines: groups where patients are supposed to talk about their feelings or discuss issues that have come up on the ward (e.g. which TV programme to watch and who is going to make the decision). The patient may be worried about the progress report in case she/he is too outspoken, but may also take the opportunity to say what she/he thinks about it all. Routine administrations of certain drugs, particularly tranquillisers and sleeping tablets.

A junior psychiatrist is usually directly in charge of the case (yes, that's what the patient has become by now). There is also a senior psychiatrist who comes perhaps weekly. On that day there is the weekly performance of the 'ward round' and of case conferences, where patients are asked to talk about themselves in front of about 10 to 20 people, or are talked about in their absence.

This is where the decisions about the patient's future management are made.

Patients react in different ways to the environment of a mental hospital, e.g.:

- withdrawing into their inner world

- rebelling against the staff

- accepting the humble status and roles assigned to them and becoming institutionalised

- undergoing a type of conversion experience, as a result of which they become overcompliant, echoing the terminology of staff, trying to please staff, or to get away, by superficially getting 'better'.

To be *staff* — in particular a nurse — in a mental hospital can be a tough job: exposure to disturbance, dishing out unsatisfactory treatments, working in unpleasant environments with rigid hierarchies, inadequate training, little supervision, bad pay, not much social status and little influence on management decisions. Psychiatric staff can suffer as much as some of their patients — some of the staff are as 'chronic' as those they are supposed to treat and look after. After having worked in a mental hospital for some time, staff may have doubts as to what side they are on.

In order to clarify this to themselves they often resort to the use of authority: they come down heavy on the patient in an attempt to assert their own 'sanity' (*We* make the decisions here').

There is a tendency for psychiatric staff to rationalise their day-to-day decisions as being 'therapeutic' for the patient, although often it is obvious that these decisions are made simply for the staff's convenience. For example, sleeping tablets: 'It's good for you to have a good night's sleep (and it makes my job easier)' . Or 'You should have some exercise — will you sweep the kitchen floor ?'

Occasionally staff have to remind themselves that mental hospitals aren't for the benefit of the staff alone. But they also have to avoid becoming mere servants to the patient.

Staff feel torn between treating the patient as a human being or as 'a case of....' — the boundary is not clearly defined. Those staff who take a special interest in their patients are soon proved 'wrong' by their colleagues: the staff need to be experienced by patients as a 'united front', so there is often not much room for personal contact. Patients who manage to have personal contact with one or more of the staff may be seen by other staff as 'splitting the staff' and the patients will probably suffer for it.

Patients and staff can stay in a mental hospital anything from days to a lifetime.

Referral to other agency

If the psychiatrist thinks that he cannot do anything for his patient but that someone else might, he may refer him to another specialist: another psychiatrist, a specialist doctor, social worker, priest or voluntary agency (e.g. self-help groups such as Alcoholics Anonymous).

The reasons for such referrals: to get another opinion, or a re-definition of the problem; not knowing what to do; feeling unqualified to give a certain treatment; getting rid of an awkward patient.

To patients these referrals can become quite farcical: they may find themselves being sent from a psychiatrist to physician to social worker back to psychiatrist. The psychiatrist thinks there may be something physically wrong with the patient and sends him to a heart specialist. The heart specialist can't find anything wrong but thinks there may well be a 'social' problem and refers the patient to a social worker. The social worker re-defines the problem as psychological and refers the patient back to the psychiatrist.

One well-known game without end is where the psychiatrist insists that a particular complaint is 'physical' and the medical doctor that 'it's all in the mind', somewhat reversing the traditional roles.

Outcome and follow-up process, discharge and prognosis:

All psychiatrists are faced with the difficult task of how to assess improvement or change. Has the patient really got 'better'? How can improvements best be measured? Psychiatrists feel the need to objectify the results of their work with the patient: to prove to themselves and those who employ them that they are actually doing something worthwhile.

There are various ways in which the change can be measured:

First, in terms of presenting problems or symptoms: have they disappeared, are they still present, if so, to what degree, have other symptoms appeared etc.

Second, by looking at the patient's *overall performance:* this can be 'measured' (so some psychiatrists believe) by looking at a number of parameters signifying social adaptation and adjustment e.g. ability to hold down a job, not to get into trouble with the police or law, to have at least one stable relationship with a member of the opposite sex, not to fart in public. And many more! Many parameters can be used, depending on the beliefs and concerns of the psychiatrist — a homosexual psychiatrist may very well regard some of his homosexual patients as well adjusted, whereas his Freudian colleague may continue to see these patients as ill.

Third, by relying on the patient's *subjective experience* of feeling better. Many psychiatrists regard such data as unreliable and unscientific: the patient may have all sorts of motives for pretending change, or he may be deluded about his perception of change ('I'm sane because I'm the US President').

Fourth, by using so-called *objective methods* such as blood tests, measurement of body fluids, or of electrical currents in the brain. Some questionnaires are claimed to be objective scientific instruments. Whether they are and whether they are useful or not, are matters of some controversy.

Fifth, by relying on *other people's assessment* of progress e.g. family ('Now he is taking an interest in the kids again') G.P. or other professional dealing with the patient.

Psychiatrists will discharge their patients when they have fulfilled some criteria of being 'better'. Not many psychiatrists and patients believe these days in total cures — and it is difficult to determine at what point of the 'getting better process' to terminate treatment. Should the psychiatrist continue to keep an eye on his patient, even after discharge, and check up at six-monthly or yearly intervals?

Psychiatrists usually can't help making a prognosis — although they may not tell their patients what it is. To make a prognosis means to assess whether the patient is likely to get better, remain ill or become ill again.   It's guess work.

PSYCHIATRY IN THE 1980s

Community Care

Psychiatry is now more firmly established than ever before. In Britain, a Royal College of Psychiatrists has formed to which aspiring psychiatrists can be admitted after completing formal training and a number of exams.

Psychiatry as a social institution in Britain has been empowered through the Mental Health Acts which Parliament has passed. During the 19th century there were over 20 Acts or Amendment Acts relating to mental disorder. The Lunacy Act of 1890 had perhaps the most powerful effect on the subsequent treatment of the mentally ill. One major stipulation was that no patient could be admitted to a mental hospital except by magistrate's order. Only in 1930, with the Mental Treatment Act, could psychiatric patients again be admitted on a voluntary basis.

In the context of psychiatric innovations (ECT, tranquillisers and other new drugs) and in response to pressures for change in patterns of care and ways of thinking, a Royal Commission was set up in 1954 which eventually resulted in the 1959 Mental Health Act.

The new Act had three major aims:

1) To decrease the number of involuntary patients
2) To introduce 'community care'
3) To integrate psychiatric care with physical care

During the past 20 years compulsory admissions have decreased as a proportion of total admissions from 20% to 10%. The term community care is now on everybody's lips, but little has happened to introduce measures which would improve the standards of life for the majority of the mentally ill. Although the most recent 1983 Mental Health Act has gone a little further by placing a legal obligation to provide aftercare facilities on local authorities very little has been done to ensure that local authorities are able to provide employment, specialised accommodation, social and other support.

The 'move into the community' (decarceration) is the slogan of psychiatry in the 1980s. What precisely this 'community' is, nobody seems to know. Communities as such may have existed when psychiatry was born but it is no longer a meaningful concept in the modern urban world.

Until the 1960s the large institution was the main response to the problems posed by the mentally ill. Since then we have seen a sharp fall in the number of in-patients and the asylums have been criticised as 'total institutions'.

There are a number of reasons for decarceration.

Economic: The hope that considerable savings can be made.

Humanistic: The hope that better conditions for the mentally ill may be found in the 'community'.

Psychiatric: The advent of injectable drugs means that mental symptoms can be chemically controlled on a basis of monthly treatment.

Medico-political: The move to establish psychiatric units in general hospitals can be seen as the final step of the psychiatric profession to integrate itself with the rest of medicine and so guarantee its status.

Community care unfortunately means the 'integration of the sick' — not the sane. It is not seen as a problem for all, requiring change and adaptation all round, but rather as containing the insane within existing social arrangements.

The result of this short-sighted community care policy is that new 'back wards' are created in the slums of the cities. Many of those expelled from mental hospitals get lost in the traditional resorts for the 'down and out' — reception centres, railway arches, hostels, parks and so on. Young psychotics discharged into the nightmare of the large cities find themselves the prey of street criminals or a source of nuisance and alarm to others.

Community care will also have to cope with the problem of the elderly psychiatric patients who account for a large proportion of patients in the chronic wards of large mental hospitals, and are often in need of medical care for physical ailments.

Whilst the idea of community care, the open-door system, was exciting, the practice left much to be desired. The term 'decarceration', inspired by Foucault and coined by Scull (see reference p.171 or 173), means the opposite of 'incarceration': getting people out of prison-like institutions. This term in fact is shorthand for a state-sponsored policy of closing down asylums without providing an adequate alternative. The 'Italian Experiment' was the first attempt to systematically close down the large mental hospitals and discharge the mental patients into the community.

1961: 113,000 patients in Italy's mental hospitals, most compulsorily detained, average length of stay 15 years.

1982: 36,000 patients, average stay between 15 and 20 days.

1978: Italian Mental Health Act (Law 180) banned the admission and readmission of psychiatric patients to large mental hospitals. It also prevented the building of new psychiatric wards and set limits on the admission of psychiatric patients to general hospitals.

Hospital staff had to be deployed within community-based mental health centres.

Despite some impressive results in a pioneering project (called Psychiatrica Democratica) in Trieste, elsewhere in Italy the alternative facilities have not materialised.

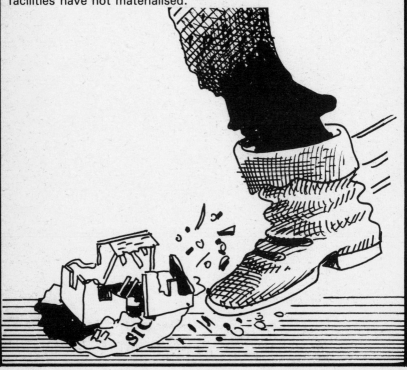

There is then a dilemma which current planners have to face: if it is wrong to get patients out of mental hospitals, and wrong to keep them in, what is to be done with them?

The Psychiatric Team

By law and by tradition, the social response to mental disorder is dominated by the medical profession. Ultimate statutory and clinical responsibility lies with the doctor. Within the psychiatric profession there is a rigid hierarchical structure: the most senior doctor is usually, because of many other commitments (administration, research, possibly private practice) only peripherally involved in the day-to-day care of his patients — he depends on the reports of the nursing and junior medical staff. More recently the 'multidisciplinary team' has emerged, headed by the psychiatrist. Its various members are

psychiatrist: trained as a medical doctor and then specialised in psychiatry. His/her task is to diagnose and treat disorders, illnesses and deficiencies of the human mind. He/she may subscribe to any of the psychiatric approaches outlined earlier.

psychologist: has studied psychological processes and behaviour in general, and then specialised in clinical psychology. His/her tasks include clinical assessment and diagnostic testing, the application of certain treatments (e.g. behaviour therapy, sometimes some form of psychotherapy) and their evaluation.

psychotherapist: any person who practises some kind of psychotherapy (see p.53) no matter what his/her professional background is. Psychotherapists can be lay persons, doctors, psychologists, social workers — the one thing they have in common is some form of psychotherapy training.

psychoanalyst: a professional, not necessarily a doctor, but usually recruited from the helping professions (see pp.40-52), who has received a training in psychoanalysis at a recognised institute and who has undergone many years of a personal analysis, who practises psychoanalysis, usually not in public psychiatric services but privately.

psychiatric social worker: a qualified social worker who has specialised in working with the mentally disordered. Duties include social and psychological support of clients, statutory involvement in some admissions (see p.148), securing housing and welfare benefits.

psychiatric nurse: male or female nurse with special training in psychiatry, based in hospitals or community. Duties range from well-defined therapeutic roles, to key holders in large mental hospitals. Community psychiatric nurses (CPN's) supervise reintegration of long-term in-patients into the community, by giving psychological support and/or injections of tranquillisers for chronic patients.

occupational therapist: a very flexible role depending on the ethos of the institution. May simply keep patient occupied while in mental hospital (which might mean basket making). However in many hospitals the O.T. has a much more active role in the rehabilitation of patients: manual work, household management, etc.

art therapist: usually with a special training in the use of arts for therapy e.g. music-dance-, art- and drama-therapists.

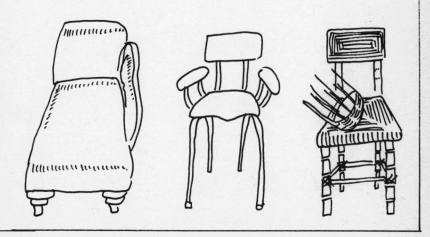

The boundaries of psychiatry

Although still firmly in the grip of psychiatrists the multidisciplinary approach presents a potential threat to psychiatrists. If professionals from other disciplines gradually develop similar skills to psychiatrists, what then will remain of the psychiatrists' special expertise? What will become of their monopoly?

There are some signs that the response to mental disorder might become de-medicalised. There are an increasing number of non-medical private and public settings that deal with psychiatric patients, e.g. counselling services. New non-medical training schemes in psychotherapy, new administrative structures empowering non-medical staff to be in charge of, for instance, Child Guidance Clinics also threaten the medical monopoly. Some psychological problems in children are being increasingly re-defined as 'educational'.

The medics argue that mental problems are evidence of mental illness and only specialists for illness — doctors — can deal with them. Their opponents say that if mental problems are seen as human predicaments, then why should doctors be better equipped to deal with them than non-doctors?

On the other hand the 'psychiatrisation' of life has led over time to a situation where problems formerly not defined as mental have come under the jurisdiction of the psychiatric profession. One result of defining and labelling deviant behaviour as an illness is that 'badness' is translated into 'sickness' and therefore requiring 'treatment' rather than punishment.

Whereas a bad person is thought of as being responsible for his behaviour, the ill person can claim diminished responsibility. But who is to decide where madness ends and badness starts?

Psychiatry has been offered and has taken this role — another example of its continuous expansion and invasion of more and more aspects of life.

But the image of psychiatrists as those competent to pass a judgement on the 'criminal responsibility' of people accused of murder has taken a number of blows in recent years. In a climate of opinion where retribution is demanded, there is much confusion in this area. Perhaps 'mad' and 'bad' are different ways of describing the same thing. Each society and social group has its own selective awareness of what are its problems. What is 'madness' to the psychiatrist may be 'unreliability' to the employer, 'evil' to the civil servant, 'male chauvinist' to the feminist, 'stupid' to the clever, 'illogical' or 'unreasonable' to the philosopher and so forth.

Psychiatry as a social institution

Psychiatry is financed by local and central government, and/or insurance systems in some countries, and therefore compromises have to be made between 'saving money' and 'saving patients', between satisfying the state and satisfying the individual recipients of psychiatric services. Most ruling systems or societies are interested in the unproblematic and effective running of their services. This is why approaches which at least appear to be simple, straightforward, reassuring, time-saving and *'cost-effective'* are in favour. Drug treatment seems to fulfil these criteria nowadays (much as did custodial care in the past) and it is therefore deemed acceptable that it is largely paid for by public money: drug treatment has become 'socialised'.

In this context it is hardly surprising that psychotherapy has not become a standard form of treatment: it demands a lot of time from therapist and client, it tends to confront problems rather than suppress them, it is less simple and therefore less measurable, and it doesn't help big private business. Whether psychotherapists liked it or not, psychotherapy itself had to become a private enterprise (except in those relatively few cases where it is state-resourced).

168

Let us look at 'psychiatry' as a 'public repair business' and continue to draw parallels between the organisation of business and that of psychiatry. One of the basic principles of setting up a successful business and being highly cost-effective is to isolate various areas of demand and to develop standard procedures and techniques to deal with each area — the closer to mass-production and mass-administration the better.

The way that psychiatry organises itself reflects this. Psychiatric services seen in terms of demand and supply raise the following questions:

The demand: This is almost impossible to assess: should it be based on 'psychiatric morbidity' in the general population? How can it reliably be established? What are the criteria? How does real morbidity relate to identified morbidity: should psychiatry make itself available to everyone who has some kind of disturbance? Who hasn't? Psychiatry for everybody is an infinite demand.

The supply: Psychiatric services are supplied in the patient's home, in out-patient departments of general hospitals or special mental hospitals. And of course in private practice. The reality is that demand is much in excess of supply; this means waiting lists, rapid treatments, little time for individual patients, etc.

Question: If there were no supply of psychiatry would there be a demand for it? Has psychiatry created new needs, in the same way that other consumer goods have?

Answer: What comes first: the chicken or the egg?

In order to respond more economically to the demand, psychiatry has divided itself into specialised departments. These are:

Adult psychiatry:
A wide range of mental patients aged 18-65.

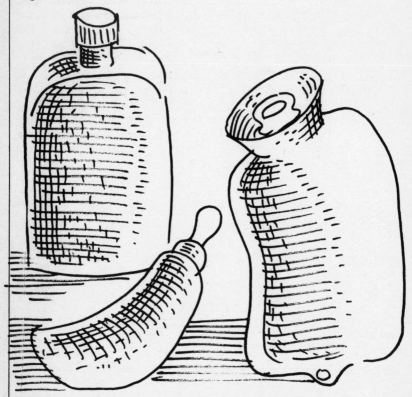

Child psychiatry:
Children up to 18 and often their families.

Psychogeriatrics:
Patients over 65, mostly suffering from dementia (physical symptoms as well) — almost half the mental hospital beds are occupied by demented patients.

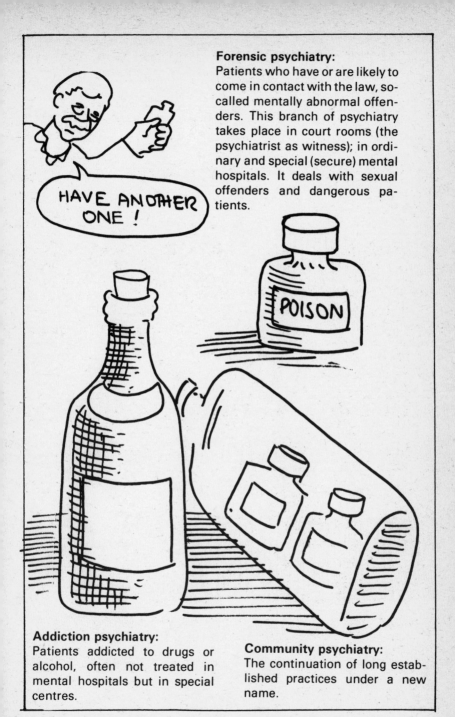

Forensic psychiatry:
Patients who have or are likely to come in contact with the law, so-called mentally abnormal offenders. This branch of psychiatry takes place in court rooms (the psychiatrist as witness); in ordinary and special (secure) mental hospitals. It deals with sexual offenders and dangerous patients.

Addiction psychiatry:
Patients addicted to drugs or alcohol, often not treated in mental hospitals but in special centres.

Community psychiatry:
The continuation of long established practices under a new name.

Further Reading

Many books have been written on many different aspects of psychiatry. The following is therefore an inexcusably arbitrary list of straight and less straight books on the subject.

General Issues

Bateson, G.: *Steps to an Ecology of Mind.* Paladin 1973.

Dörner, K.: *Madmen and the Bourgeoisie. Social History of Insanity and Psychiatry.* Blackwell 1984.

Foucault, M.: *Mental Illness and Psychology.* Harper + Row, Repr. 1976.

Laing, R. D.: *The Divided Self.* Tavistock 1960. Penguin 1965.

Szasz, T. S.: *The Myth of Mental Illness.* Paladin 1972.

Goffman, E.: *Asylums.* Penguin 1968.

Scull, A.: *Museums of Madness.* Penguin 1982.

Clare, A.: *Psychiatry in Dissent.* Tavistock 1976

Ingleby, D. (ed.): *Critical Psychiatry.* Penguin 1981.

Brain/Mind

Rose, S.: *The Conscious Brain.* Pelican, rev. ed. 1976.

Blakemore, C.: *Mechanics of the Mind.* Cambridge Univ. Press 1977.

Luria, A.R.: *The Working Brain.* Penguin 1973.

Lishman, W.A.: *Organic Psychiatry.* Blackwell 1978.

Ornstein, R.E.: *The Psychology of Consciousness.* Penguin 1975.

Psychodynamics

Laplanche, J., J.B. Pontalis: *The Language of Psychoanalysis* (Dictionary) Hogarth Press 1973.

Brown, D., J. Pedder: *Introduction to Psychotherapy.* Tavistock 1979.

Malan, D.H.: *Individual Psychotherapy and the Science of Psychodynamics.* Butterworth 1979.

Kopp, S.: *If you meet the Buddha on the Road, kill Him.* Sheldon Press 1974.

Yalom, I.D.: *Theory and Practice of Group Psychotherapy.* Basic Books 1975.

Herink, R.: (ed.) *The Psychotherapy Handbook: A Guide to more than 250 different therapies in use today.* New American Library 1980.

Behaviour Therapy

Meyer, V., E.S. Chesser: *Behaviour Therapy in Clinical Practice.* Penguin 1970.

Systemic Approach

Hoffman, L.: *Foundations of Family Therapy.* Basic Books 1981.

Watzlawick, P., J. Beavin and D.D. Jackson: *Pragmatics of Human Communication.* W.W. Norton 1967.

Minuchin, S.: *Families and Family Therapy.* Tavistock 1974.

Selvini Palazzoli, M., et al.: *Paradox and Counterparadox.* J. Aronson 1978.

Haley, J.: *Problem-Solving Therapy.* Jossey-Bass 1976.

Treacher, A., J. Carpenter: *Using Family Therapy.* Blackwell 1984.

Psychopathology

Kräupl Taylor, F.: *Psychopathology.* Quatermaine House, rev. 1979.

Textbook

Kaplan, H., B. Saddock: *Modern Synopsis of Comprehensive Textbook of Psychiatry 4.* 4th edition, Williams and Wilkins 1985.

Notes on author and artist

Eia Asen grew up in Berlin. He read medicine at the universities of Berlin, Heidelberg and Innsbruck and qualified as a doctor in 1971. He went to London in 1972, read Social Psychology at the London School of Economics and trained as a psychiatrist at the Maudsley Hospital from 1974-78. He has since worked in an NHS day clinic in London, specialising in the application of the systemic approach.

Bernard Canavan grew up in Co Longford, Ireland and has worked as an illustrator and painter since he came to London in the 1960s. He also has a degree in Philosophy, Politics and Economics from Oxford and has produced *Economists for Beginners* in this series.

Acknowledgement:

We would very much like to thank *Barry Richards* and *Heiner Schuff* for their invaluable help.